D1291631

SOME ASPECTS OF
MEDICAL GEOGRAPHY

UNIVERSITY OF LONDON
HEATH CLARK LECTURES 1962
delivered at
The London School of Hygiene and Tropical Medicine

Some Aspects of Medical Geography

By

L. DUDLEY STAMP

C.B.E., D.Sc., D.Lit., LL.D., Ekon.D., D.Sc.Nat.

*Professor Emeritus of Social Geography
in the University of London*

LONDON
OXFORD UNIVERSITY PRESS
NEW YORK   TORONTO
1964

Oxford University Press, Amen House, London E.C.4

GLASGOW   NEW YORK   TORONTO   MELBOURNE   WELLINGTON
BOMBAY   CALCUTTA   MADRAS   KARACHI   LAHORE   DACCA
CAPE TOWN   SALISBURY   NAIROBI   IBADAN   ACCRA
KUALA LUMPUR   HONG KONG

PRINTED IN GREAT BRITAIN

CONTENTS

1

CLIMATE AND DISEASE

IT was with considerable trepidation that I accepted the invitation to deliver the Heath Clark Lectures. I felt greatly honoured to receive the invitation, but doubted sincerely my qualifications to accept. Although in the course of my university career I have collected doctorates in science, literature, laws and economics, I have no claim whatsoever to medical knowledge or training. It is a case therefore of rushing in where galaxies of medical angels have feared to tread, and I can only hope my medical colleagues will pardon my *gaffes*.

In the field which is being called, for want of a better term, medical geography, I believe there are great opportunities, too long neglected, for the advancement of knowledge. What I hope to show is the geographical approach to the analysis of data. The medical data I must accept as they are. I am fully aware that my medical colleagues will say the facts available are inadequate, and may even be misleading. It may even be that the geographical analysis will reveal further imperfections.

In common with bodies of data in other fields, published figures of mortality and morbidity may be studied and analysed in two contrasted and complementary ways. They may, and normally are, analysed statistically and the steady refinement in methods of statistical analysis yields constantly ever more illuminating results.

But the data may also be studied and analysed cartographically by being recorded in different ways and according to different methods on maps. The maps should perhaps more strictly be called cartograms since they are simplified maps specially designed to show clearly or to highlight selected facts and to permit comparisons and correlations.

Any map showing the distribution of a given phenomenon or a given set of facts becomes in essence a factual document. It explains nothing; on the contrary, it inevitably poses a series of questions. Above all any such map automatically asks the question, Why? So we are forced to seek an explanation of the pattern, often complex and puzzling, which the map reveals. We are led to seek possible correlations with factors known or believed to be responsible. In so doing we need to construct other maps showing the distribution of such factors. Here a scientific approach is vital. We must be prepared to examine a wide range of causative factors but equally prepared to discard any tentative correlation or preconceived hypothesis. To a considerable extent maps must be treated as waste paper or certainly no more than a graphic notebook. It is when the examination of all suspected factors fails to afford a satisfactory solution that real research begins: the detection of the hitherto unsuspected causes. It is in this direction that geographical analysis may be able to make a real contribution to knowledge.

We may conveniently consider cartographical analysis on at least four levels.

The first level is the world level. To this belong the various attempts which have been made to show the world distribution of major diseases. Outstanding in this field is the collection of seventeen sheets of coloured maps prepared under the direction of Dr. Jacques M. May—himself a doctor of medicine—and his research team at the American Geographical Society and published by the Society. The maps were issued with the regular quarterly numbers of the *Geographical Review* and are fully annotated as well as described briefly in the *Review*. In addition Dr. May has published a comprehensive work *The Ecology of Human Disease* as the first of three large volumes, two published within the last few months, entitled *Studies in Medical Geography*.

Although many other factors are involved, even a casual study of these world maps makes it clear that climate plays a dominant role. I propose in the latter part of this lecture to look at this aspect in more detail.

The second level of cartographic analysis may be called the continental. Few species of animals or plants are world wide in distribution even within the climatic belts most favourable to them. Without the intervention of man they tend to be restricted to marked zoo-geographical regions or provinces, and a wider distribution is commonly due to the accidental or deliberate action of man. This is broadly true of the organisms causing disease and of their vectors. The New World and the Old are separated by the Atlantic; Australia is an island continent imperfectly linked by islands with Asia; Africa south of the Sahara is cut off by sea and desert from other regions. Man, in particular the European settler of the past three or four centuries, has been slow to recognize that in each major area Nature had worked out a biological balance which he could all too easily upset by thoughtless introductions. The rabbit in Australia is a familiar example: in the absence of natural or adequate enemies its multiplication was fantastic till myxomatosis stepped in. Less well known, but perhaps as disastrous, has been the spread of a giant snail which causes huge crop losses in many countries and the spread of which is not disconnected with its supposed qualities, when cooked, as an aphrodisiac. The disastrous results of the introduction of a disease, possibly one of minor virulence in its home area, into a country where the people had no inbuilt resistance is well known even if underemphasized. In number of victims no plague the world has ever known begins to touch the 12–13 million victims claimed by influenza in India in 1918–19.

The third level of study, perhaps the most important, is the national. Each country, even the underdeveloped, has its own medical and health services, each its own means and methods of collecting statistics, though there are often strange contrasts even between one country and its neighbours. Further, we are all naturally interested primarily in our own country and what is happening there. Britain, through the Registrar-General, has a mass of material available for study and some pioneer though important attempts have been made to use it. But we are especially indebted to Lord Nathan,[1] who, as Chairman of a Joint Committee of the Royal Geographical Society and the British Medical Association, was able to secure facilities and funds for a *National Atlas of Disease Mortality* the preparation of which under Dr. Melvyn Howe of Aberystwyth was completed in November 1962 (published October 1963).

The fourth level may be called the local—the incidence of disease in a given locality which may be a local government area such as a municipality, a conurbation, a rural district, a housing estate—perhaps even the domain (or is it sphere of influence?) of a single general

---

[1] Lord Nathan took the Chair at the first of these Lectures.

practitioner. I shall refer later to some of the epochal discoveries made in the past by detailed mapping at this level. Today I believe it to be a very neglected line of research and one which is crying out for investigators.

In the remainder of this lecture I propose to give some examples of each of these levels of geographical mapping, but before doing so, will mention the plan for the other three lectures.

In the second lecture I am emboldened by reading the exact terms of the Trust Deed setting up these Heath Clark Lectures which 'shall include the . . . humanistic aspects of . . . preventive medicine . . . both in temperate and tropical climates' to attempt to deal with the very difficult and still little understood relationships between climate and health.

To the layman it may sometimes be that a map is just a map. But used as a research tool maps are of many kinds and the same data may be expressed cartographically in many different ways. When one is searching for causes and explanations, there is no one single type of map but, instead, a wide possible range. In my third lecture I propose to deal especially with some of the problems involved in mapping and to illustrate with specific examples.

Being convinced that much work lies ahead and that there are fruitful lines of investigation awaiting workers, I propose to use my privilege as one now retired from active university teaching to outline some of these problems as I see them, pointing out those that seem to me to be urgent, and how indeed we may at the present time be making serious blunders through our lack of understanding.

Turning now to the world distribution of some

common or well-known diseases, I must obviously refer first to the work of Dr. Jacques May and his *Atlas of Diseases*. The seventeen sheets of the *Atlas* comprise:

Plate 1. World Distribution of Poliomyelitis, 1900–50.
  2. Distribution of Cholera, 1816–1950.
  3. Distribution of Malaria Vectors.
  4. Distribution of Helminthiases.
  5. Distribution of Dengue and Yellow Fever.
  6. World Distribution of Plague, 1900–52.
  7. Distribution of Leprosy, 1952.
  8. Study in Human Starvation: (1) Sources of Selected Foods.
  9. Study in Human Starvation: (2) Diets and Deficiency Diseases.
  10. World Distribution of Rickettsial Diseases: (1) Louse-borne and Flea-borne; Typhus.
  11. World Distribution of Rickettsial Diseases: (2) Tick-borne and Mite-borne Forms.
  12. World Distribution of Rickettsial Diseases: (3) Tick and Mite Vectors.
  13. Explored Areas of Arthropod-borne Viral Infections.
  14. World Distribution of Leishmaniases.
  15. World Distribution of Spirochetal Diseases: (1) Yaws, Pinta, Bejel.
  16. World Distribution of Spirochetal Diseases: (2) Relapsing Fevers: Louse-borne and Tick-borne.
  17. World Distribution of Spirochetal Diseases: (3) Leptospiroses.

Although each map sheet is self-explanatory, giving full bibliographies and sources both general and regional, Dr. May's three large volumes, already mentioned, form the essential commentary. A tremendous amount of work has gone into the preparation of these maps and it is, perhaps, impossible to do more than suggest what they show.

In the first place, many gaps must be due to lack of information; but blank areas of great extent in many cases coincide with uninhabited country—notably the great tropical and subtropical deserts.

The marked prevalence, in the second place, of so many diseases in tropical Africa, South-east Asia, and tropical South America is clearly linked with paucity of medical services: they are the underdeveloped areas of the world. Overpopulation compared with existing levels of resource development is also brought out in some areas.

Making full allowance, however, for these factors, it still remains obvious that the world's hot regions, broadly the tropics, favour the wide spread of various human diseases.

It has frequently been pointed out—as by Buchanan and Pugh in Nigeria—that human diseases, as an environmental factor in national or regional development, fall into three groups.

First, there are diseases common to mankind in any climate and in any state of prosperity—such as measles, mumps, chickenpox, tuberculosis, various types of heart disease, many forms of cancer, venereal diseases, pneumonia, and so on.

Secondly, there are diseases associated with low standards of living, nutrition, and hygiene—smallpox, typhus, trachoma, perhaps poliomyelitis, &c.

Thirdly, there are the specifically tropical diseases.

Dwellers in the tropics, it is often forgotten, suffer from most of the diseases affecting the denizens of cooler lands together with many more peculiarly their own. Because of the proneness of tropical lands to all the three groups of diseases, many writers have pointed

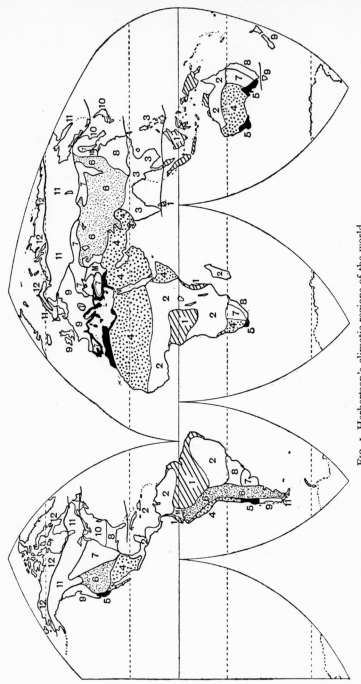

FIG. 1. Herbertson's climatic regions of the world.

Climatic regions of low latitudes: 1. equatorial; 2. tropical; 3. tropical monsoon; 4. hot deserts and semi-deserts. Climates of middle and high latitudes are numbered 5–12.

[*Chisholm's Handbook of Commercial Geography* (1960), 16th ed., London, Longmans, Green & Co. Modified by Stamp.]

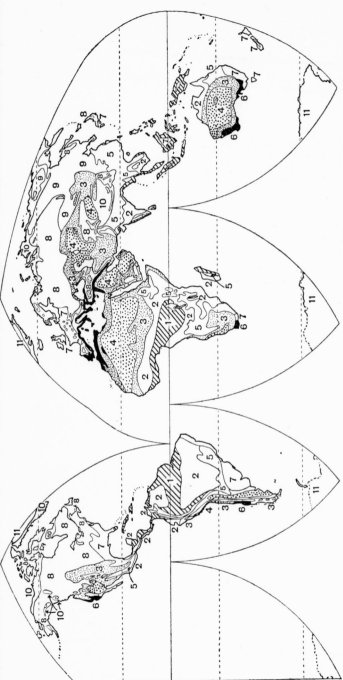

FIG. 2. Köppen's climatic regions of the world.

A. Tropical rain climates: 1. hot, wet forest climate; 2. periodically dry savanna climate.
B. Dry climates: 3. steppe climate; 4. desert climate.
C. Warm temperate rain climates: 5. warm winter-dry climate; 6. warm summer-dry climate; 7. cool temperate climate.
Climates of middle and high latitudes are numbered 8–11.

[*Chisholm's Handbook of Commercial Geography* (1960), 16th ed., London, Longmans, Green & Co.]

out that ill health is not the exceptional but the normal lot of the inhabitants. This is especially true of Africa: until the advent of Western medical skill the people of tropical Africa had scarcely had a chance of normal physical or mental development.

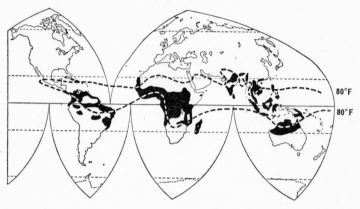

FIG. 3. The world distribution of yaws (data from May). An excellent example of an essentially tropical disease. It is caused by a spirochaete, *Treponema pertenue*, allied to the organism causing syphilis, and the sores which result closely resemble syphilitic sores. It is believed to have originated in Africa and to have been spread by slaves. The organism enters through cuts or abrasions of the skin, including insect bites. It is favoured by heat and moisture and is nearly always found on low ground. Its distribution has been linked with tropical rain forests and savannas (Regions 1, 2, and 3 of Fig. 1) but it is probable, as May says, that this is because skin lacerations under such conditions occur easily but do not heal quickly. Nevertheless, the patchy distribution remains unexplained.

According to statements made by the World Health Organization (WHO) in October 1962, there were still in the world, despite its eradication in many countries, 150 million cases of malaria. Even this was not the most prevalent disease: that place was held by the eye disease trachoma, leading to blindness, with 500 million victims essentially in the tropics. Another disease still widespread in the tropics is tuberculosis, and the hope there lies in home treatment since sufficiently numerous

hospitals do not exist and poverty would prevent the sac-
rifice of time from the essential round of toil for patients
to accept hospitalization even if facilities existed.

What would seem to be a direct influence of climate
is seen in May's map of malaria vectors—the numerous
species of *Anopheles*. A line can be drawn and is drawn
on the map on the cooler poleward side of which the
species of *Anopheles* elsewhere to be feared as vectors
no longer carry the disease.

If we look at any map of world climates we see that
the humid tropics—the equatorial, tropical, and tropical monsoon climates of Herbertson and later writers—
are bounded by two broad though discontinuous belts
of deserts and semi-deserts of the arid zone. The
deserts have diseases of their own, especially those
carried by human and animal parasites, but they are
free from the innumerable water-borne plagues. These
simple facts carry at least three obvious lessons. First,
the humid tropics are areas with adequate heat and
moisture for cultivation and may be expected both to
carry larger populations and to make larger contributions to world food supplies in the future: the conquest
of disease, already proceeding apace, is essential.
Second, the arid zones with some marked exceptions
are naturally more healthy: this may well be turned to
good account in future development. Third, water
brings life to dry lands in two senses—water permits
crop production but it may also make life dangerous,
because it is the carrier of disease. There is far too little
liaison between the irrigation engineer and the health
officer and there is a real danger of disease destroying
the very people irrigation is designed to help—as with
bilharzia.

Some of the complexities of the world distribution of disease are well illustrated if we look at cholera. The maps which follow are based on those on Plate 2 of

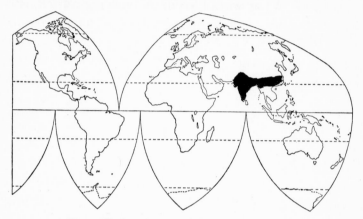

FIG. 4. Cholera: believed original area, pre-1816.

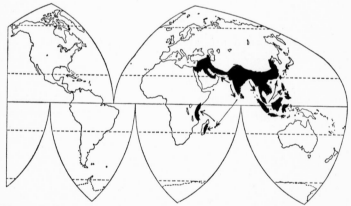

FIG. 5. Cholera: routes of pandemic 1816–23 and areas affected (after May).

Dr. May's *Atlas*. Cholera is believed to have existed in India since the beginning of recorded history, but probably nowhere else until the beginning of the nineteenth century. Fig. 4 shows cholera prior to 1816 as the

scourge of India but being spread by shipping east to
Japan, west through Mesopotamia to the shores of the

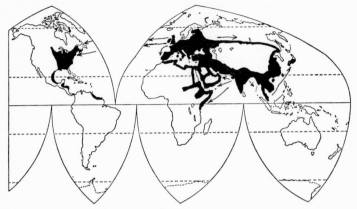

FIG. 6. Cholera: routes of pandemic 1826–37 and areas affected (after May).

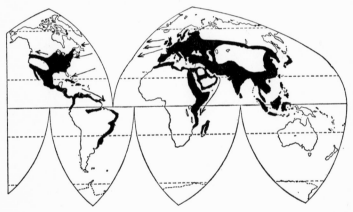

FIG. 7. Cholera: routes of pandemic 1842–62 and areas affected (after May).

Mediterranean, south-west across the Indian Ocean
to the east coast of Africa (Fig. 5).

In the period 1826–37 (Fig. 6) it spread over the whole
of Europe and was taken to North America—and these
were the bad days of cholera in Britain.

By the period 1842–62 (Fig. 7) it had found its way overland to the west coast of North America and was widespread in South America. The map of areas affected 1865–75 (Fig. 8) shows some retraction following the diffusion of knowledge of its causation but the real change is shown in the last map (Fig. 9)—the last occurrence in the Western Hemisphere in 1911, thereafter stopped by quarantine, the last occurrence in Europe in

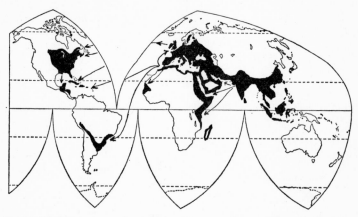

FIG. 8. Cholera: routes of pandemic 1865–75 and areas affected (after May, simplified).

1923, and so once more confined to its old cradle of pre-1816 (mainly India), but with the great epidemic in Egypt of 1947 not to be forgotten.

Cholera is a mysterious disease. On his map, published 1951, Dr. May summarizes the position by saying:

'Endemic cholera—continuous occurrence—occurs only in India and possibly in the Yuan Valley in China; epidemic cholera can occur anywhere in the world as long as susceptible man and vibrio are brought together. Factors thought to cause outbreaks are: congregation of susceptibles, high temperature,

ERRATA

Page 15, line 5 from foot, for '1848' read '1854'
Page 16, Fig. 10, for '1848' read '1854'

Stamp: Some Aspects of Medical Geography

high absolute humidity, in some places drought, in others floods. Factors thought to govern endemicity are: high temperature, low altitude, presence of water containing organic matter and salts and sheltered from the rays of the sun. Factors governing the change from quiescent vibrio to virulent vibrio and vice versa, both in man and in nature, are unknown.'

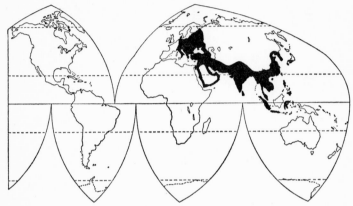

FIG. 9. Cholera: areas affected 1912–23. Last occurrence in Western Hemisphere, 1911; thereafter stopped by quarantine. Last occurrence in Europe, 1923; thereafter stopped by quarantine. Serious epidemic in Egypt, 1947. Endemic areas in India now limited to Bengal and a few coastal tracts.

What a confession of ignorance! In his book (1958) Dr. May devotes a lengthy chapter to the ecology of cholera; in particular the historical routes of four major pandemics are traced—those of 1816–23, 1826–37, 1842–62, and 1865–75. A major breakthrough in the battle against cholera was made by Dr. John Snow (1813–58), then a general practitioner in the Golden Square area of London. Over 500 deaths occurred within the space of 10 days in August and early September 1848. On a large-scale map he plotted exactly the house where each of the victims was attacked. It centred round a spot in Broad Street where there was a manual pump from which local residents obtained their drinking water. On

8 September the handle of this pump was removed at Snow's request and incidence of new cases ceased almost miraculously.

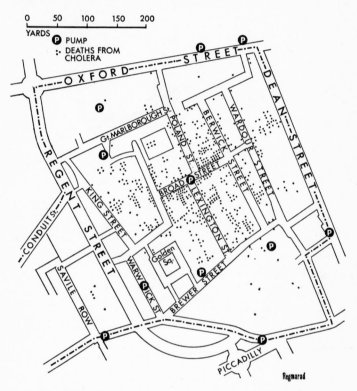

FIG. 10. Dr. John Snow's map of cholera deaths in the Soho district of London, 1848. Notice the affected pump in Broad Street.

Despite this demonstration, over a century ago, of the immediate value of detailed mapping, the geographical approach, as we shall see later, is still almost entirely neglected.

This digression has a moral. Although world maps of disease distribution are of great interest, it is in detailed work that the greatest possibilities of results lie.

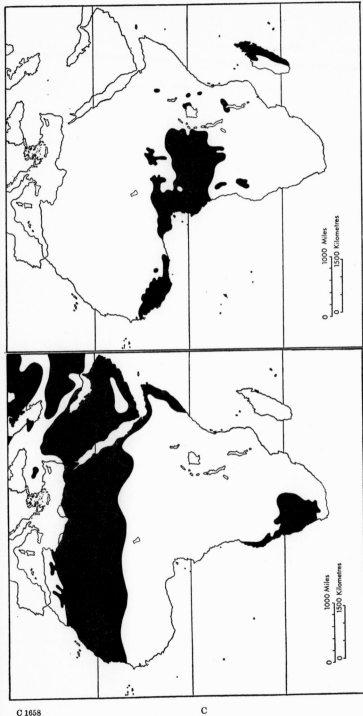

FIG. 11. The arid and wet regions of Africa. All parts in black on the left-hand map have less than 10 in. (250 mm.) of rainfall per annum; all parts in black on the right-hand map have more than 60 in. (1,500 mm.) of rainfall per annum.

C 1658

C

Because of the doubtful reliability of information from many countries world maps are bound to be incomplete, and we may with advantage turn to a single continent. Because it strides the equator and reaches both north and south into mid-latitudes, Africa is well suited to show connexions between physical environment and human health and disease: further, much has only recently come directly under the beneficial influence of Western medicine.

The tsetse fly has been stigmatized as the real ruler of Africa and with considerable and continuing justification. There are in fact some twenty species of the blood-sucking flies of the genus *Glossina*, the two most serious being *G. palpalis*, which transmits the single-celled organism *Trypanosoma gambiense*, causing sleeping sickness in man, and *Glossina morsitans*, transmitting *Trypanosoma rhodesiense*, which causes the Rhodesian form of that disease. The first disease was endemic in West Africa where the population had acquired a certain immunity, but when in the early years of this century it was carried to East Africa it gave rise to what has been described as the greatest epidemic ever recorded, killing two-thirds of the total population in some areas of Uganda within two or three years. In the few decades since, several unrelated drugs have proved so effective that the disease is no longer a menace: only small numbers of people who come for treatment too late or who are beyond the reach of medical services still die of sleeping sickness. Treatment is simple: the patient, at least in early stages, does not need to be admitted to hospital but can be treated at home by an itinerant team of minimal skill. Prophylactic treatment by injection is now usual; it gives immunity for a sufficient number of months to break the chain of infection between man and fly. But it is different with the animal population. These two and other species of *Glossina* transmit various trypanosomes causing the nagana

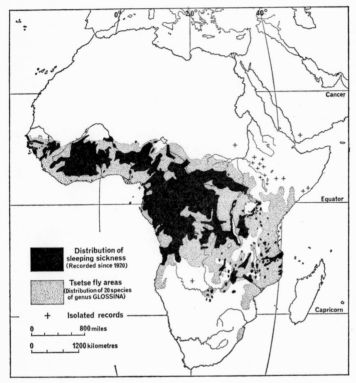

FIG. 12. The tsetse fly areas and the distribution of sleeping sickness in Africa (map prepared by the late Professor P. A. Buxton).

disease of cattle, horses, and dogs. Just as monkeys are believed to be carriers of human sleeping sickness, so may antelopes and other wild herbivores be the carriers of nagana, the fatal disease which is so serious as to prevent the rearing and keeping of cattle in the 'flybelts'. These fly-belts occur especially on the margins of bush or forestland near rivers or lakes and it is only practicable to clear such breeding grounds round villages. The flies are particularly active during the hotter parts of the day when cattle tend to rest in the

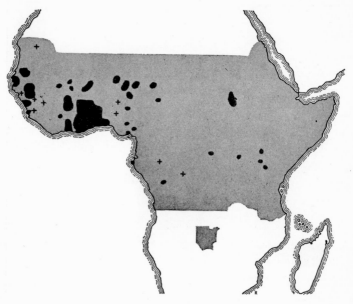

FIG. 13. Yellow fever in Africa (1930–51). The hatched area is that recognized officially by health authorities for international purposes as liable to yellow fever (delineated by the Expert Commission on Quarantine). The dark areas represent epidemic areas.
[Stamp, L. D. (1953), *Africa*, London, Chapman & Hall. After Findlay.]

shade. When the fly sucks blood from an infected animal—including wild carriers—it draws up some of the trypanosomes which then undergo a developmental phase within the fly before being passed into the blood of the animal or man on which the fly may next feed. The fly is difficult to control by insecticides because the pupae lie buried in the shady ground. The map shows the huge area affected—most of the moister parts of tropical Africa—and the best hope seems to be in breeding cattle strains which show an immunity. There is, amongst some farmers, the demand for whole-sale slaughter of game believed to be carriers, and what therefore would result in the extermination of the native fauna.

Various species of mosquito carry malaria, whilst the mosquito known as *Aëdes aegypti* carries an ultra-microscopic virus which is the cause of the dreaded yellow fever. Once the disease is contracted the victim vomits to death in nine cases out of ten. Introduced from Africa, probably by slaves, to tropical America it was yellow fever which brought to an end the attempt to build the first Panama Canal; it had to be controlled before the present Panama Canal (opened in 1914) could be constructed. The mosquito breeds in any patch of stagnant water, even that collecting at the base of fern fronds, and so wholesale clearing of large palms was tried in West Africa. Fortunately, there is a safe and effective inoculation, but when I was first working in West Africa in the early thirties this was far from being in general use and a yellow fever outbreak was a very real scare. Every now and then epidemic outbreaks occur.

Since the work of Sir Ronald Ross the life-cycle of the minute parasite causing malaria and transmitted by mosquitoes of the genus *Anopheles* is well known. The chief carrier is *A. gambiae*, widely distributed in Africa; other carriers exist over practically the whole of tropical Africa. It is probable that over very large areas of the continent all children reaching adolescence have been infected and have developed an immunity. Though apparently healthy, they have probably lost both stamina and efficiency; indeed, the danger is not so much death as debility.

Other diseases transmitted by mosquitoes include dengue or 'break-bone' fever—rarely fatal, but very painful and causing much loss of time. The enormous swelling of the legs and other parts of the body, known as elephantiasis, is caused by a minute worm transmitted by mosquitoes. It is small wonder that the World Health Organization embarked in 1961 on a world-wide campaign to eliminate malaria which had already been done successfully in a number of areas. Later I shall give some examples of malaria distribution elsewhere—in India.

Reference to the debilitating rather than fatal effects of many diseases leads naturally to a mention of hookworm. Because it is not a killing disease it has not perhaps received the attention it deserves, for it is undoubtedly a major cause of mental and bodily lethargy. The tiny worms, when adult, live in the human intestines attached to the gut wall, from which they suck blood. The continuous loss of blood leads to anaemia. The eggs of the worms leave the human body in the faeces, the larvae develop in the ground, and then enter through the skin of feet and ankles of persons walking unshod on contaminated soil. Europeans wearing shoes are rarely infected and, obviously, proper sanitation would quickly eliminate the contamination of soil, and so lead to the disappearance of ankylostomiasis—as indeed it has disappeared in many countries with rising standards of living and hygiene.

Again, because it is not a killing disease, trachoma is insufficiently emphasized though it probably affects more people than any other single disease. World-wide in its distribution, it is essentially the disease of poverty, overcrowding, and dirt, the disease of childhood which has been known, as in ancient Egypt, as long as written records exist. A form of conjunctivitis affecting the eyes, it is particularly important in causing blindness and, though often mild in early stages, lays the way open to various serious infections. In a full account of its ecology Dr. Matthieu-Jean Freyche (in J. M. May, 1958, op. cit., 271–98) considers the estimate of 6 million blind from this cause as a reasonable one. The disease is of special interest because, by way of contrast with so many others, it is associated with contaminated dust blowing in arid lands rather than with humid conditions. It is said to be almost universal among the poorer classes in Egypt and probably from thence spread westwards and gradually throughout the continent.

The mention of trachoma leads one to consider other diseases associated with arid rather than humid conditions. In a valuable chapter in *The History of Land Use in Arid Regions* which I edited for UNESCO in 1961, Dr. Paul F. Russell deals at some length with malaria and bilharziasis because both are spread by irrigation farming. Unless engineer and doctor work together the benefits conferred by providing a constant water-supply may be negatived by the spread of disease. Bilharziasis or schistosomiasis is caused by parasitic schistosome worms spread by certain freshwater snails found along canals where sanitation is poor. It is a disease which is definitely spreading and over 150 million cases in the world are estimated to occur. A single snail may produce a flourishing colony in 40 days and transmission of bilharziasis occurs in about 60 days.

Children paddling, farmers wading, women washing clothes, all become infected with this blood fluke without actually drinking the water. It is a killing disease because of the derangement of internal organs, causing

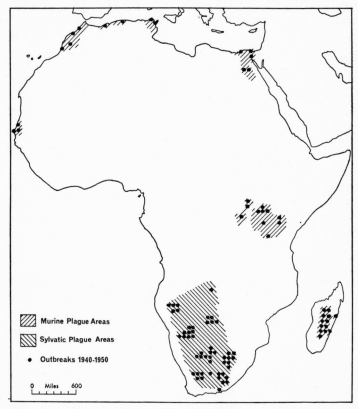

FIG. 14. Plague in Africa.

internal bleeding with the consequent discharge of blood through the rectum and bladder.

It is not my purpose here to mention all the many diseases which beset man in Africa but rather to stress the importance of noting with care and accuracy where they occur so that, having then ascertained the reasons for the distribution, the way is open to remedial measures. The map showing plague in Africa is interesting in this regard. Murine plague is transmitted from rats to man by rat fleas. The chief culprit is the domestic house-rat, *Rattus rattus*, living on (and sometimes leaving even if they are not sinking) ships which may visit the ports of Africa. The association with ports in Fig. 14 is unmistakable but this is an interesting example of a map posing a question. How did plague get to interior Kenya and Uganda? Thanks to the energetic campaigns waged against rats, plague, which caused some 15,000 deaths in and around Dakar in 1920, is now rarely a serious menace. The other form of plague, sylvatic plague, is confined to southern Africa, but that poses another problem. The permanent hosts are certainly wild rodents.

Looking again at the maps showing the distribution of malarial mosquitoes and tsetse flies in Africa, one notes of course the white areas where they do not occur. Similarly, with any map of the distribution of diseases there are the blank areas. But what do they mean? They do not *necessarily* indicate the areas where the disease or its vectors are absent, though this may be the case. It may be (*a*) that there are no records or recorded cases; (*b*) that there are no observers to make records; (*c*) that the areas are almost or entirely uninhabited, and so there are no people to be affected; or (*d*) that faulty diagnosis has failed to reveal the true position. Obviously, then, maps of world and continental scale can scarcely hope to be more than general indicators, for serious work demands detail. That is a matter I propose to reserve for consideration in my third lecture.

2

CLIMATE AND HEALTH

FORTUNATELY I need no excuse for devoting this lecture to the subject of climate and health. The Trust Deed of the Heath Clark Bequest emphasizes preventive medicine and surely one proper approach is the study of healthy communities and the factors which favour or have favoured their development. Medical men are not by any means alone in an obsession with pathological conditions: sociologists, criminologists, and town planners tend to concentrate on aberrations, abnormalities, and slums rather than to attempt the analysis of happy contented communities, uncovering the reasons for a proper state of affairs.

Indirectly the medical profession as a whole is responsible for the world's greatest problem—the rapidly increasing pressure of population on land and its resources. Doctors and nurses have already, it may be argued, made the world too healthy. Expectation of life at birth has been almost doubled in the last fifty years and is already between sixty-five and seventy in many countries of the West. In other words, every baby born into the world in one such country may look forward to a life of nearly seventy years *on average*. The old killing diseases have largely been conquered: the main unconquered enemy is now cancer, apart from the range of fatal ills which are themselves largely the result of modern conditions of life. Put into other words, the spread of the knowledge and practice of *death control* has overtaken the knowledge and practice of *birth control*. Over the world as a whole the doctor has outstripped both public opinion and the social worker. The birth-rate shows, in most countries, little change; it is the death-rate which is falling. Amongst the consequences of this, two are outstanding. One is the changing age-structure of populations. In many countries one person in every seven or eight qualifies on grounds of age to be an 'old age pensioner'. What nonsense this makes of the political cry in Britain! Every year a *smaller* number of workers in the active wage-earning group has to support a *larger* number of 'retired' folk. But a second, even more serious, consequence is the rapid increase of population all over the world. World population now exceeds 3,150 millions. In a paper published as recently as 1950 Sir Julian Huxley ventured to suggest that the world population was probably increasing by 0·8 per cent. per annum, perhaps by 1 per cent., and that world population by A.D. 2000 might reach 3,000 millions. In fact we have already passed that total in 1962 and we *know* from modern census returns, not just from estimates, that the annual rate of increase, going up every year, is now 1·8 per cent. This means over 55 million additional mouths to be fed every year—and, one should add, 55 million additional brains and pairs of hands to work.

Contrary to popular belief, the highest *rates* of increase are not in those crowded countries of monsoon Asia, notably India and China, where it has been so long the custom to refer to the 'teeming millions'. Countries with *more* than the world average of net increase include practically the whole of the Americas, probably most of Africa, as well as the new lands of

Australasia. Because of their huge initial total the Asiatic countries, though with a lower rate, show annually enormous additions in sheer numbers. Nevertheless, from an estimated 66·4 per cent. of the world's people in 1800 Asia has dropped to *c.* 58 per cent. in 1960, whereas the Americas have risen from 2·8 per cent. to 13·5. Almost without exception the countries of Europe, already crowded from the Middle Ages onwards, are showing less than world average increase. Including immigrants, Britain adds now between 200,000 and 250,000 to its 50 millions—of the order of 0·5 per cent. or rather less.

If we plot on a map of the world the figures for the expectation of life, we might therefore expect to get a general measure of 'healthiness' of the people. Although figures are available for most European countries, they do not exist for a large part of the world. Most of those available in the *Demographic Yearbook* of the United Nations are given below in Table I which compares *c.* 1900 with *c.* 1950. Other major countries for which recent figures only exist include: The Congo, 39; Egypt, 36 (1936–8, probably now considerably higher); South Africa, whites 67, Asians 55; Ceylon, 59; Thailand, 51; Italy, 68; Portugal, 62; Costa Rica, 56; Mexico, 38 (1940, doubtless higher now); Argentina, 59; Chile, 52; Ecuador, 50.

What one really has here is a measure of the extent and effectiveness of medical and health services. As A. Leslie Banks, Professor of Human Ecology in the University of Cambridge, observed in a paper to the Royal Geographical Society in 1959, the world can be divided into contrasted parts—those countries effectively served by modern medical skill and the others.

In the first group, as suggested by Table I, the age-old biblical statement that the days of man are three score years and ten is as near the truth as it is possible to get. The most progressive countries have, broadly speaking,

TABLE I

Expectation of life at Birth, by Sex
c. 1900 and c. 1950

Country	Male			Female		
	c. 1900	c. 1950	Gain in years	c. 1900	c. 1950	Gain in years
Austria	39	62	23	41	67	26
Belgium	45	62	17	49	67	18
Denmark	53	68	15	56	70	14
England and Wales	49	66	17	52	71	19
Finland	45	63	18	48	70	22
France	45	64	19	49	69	20
Germany, West	45	65	20	48	68	20
Hungary	37	59	22	38	63	25
Iceland	48	66	18	53	70	17
India	23	32	9	24	32	8
Ireland	49	65	16	50	67	17
Japan	44	61	17	45	65	20
Netherlands	51	71	20	53	73	20
New Zealand	58	68	10	61	72	11
Northern Ireland	47	65	18	47	69	22
Norway	55	69	14	58	73	15
Spain	34	59	25	36	64	28
Sweden	55	69	14	57	72	15
Switzerland	49	66	17	52	71	19
Trinidad and Tobago	37	60	23	39	63	24
United States	48	65	17	51	71	20

the best expectation of life: in that sense they are the healthiest. But they are all, it may be noted, in mid-latitudes, in the so-called temperate zone.

Some years ago S. F. Markham attempted to express in a book entitled *Climate and the Energy of Nations* what were, and indeed still are, some popular conceptions. He showed the gradual trend of the great centres of world civilization to have moved progressively away from the tropics and warm temperate regions—of the Indus Valley, Babylon, Nineveh and Egypt to Crete, Greece, and Rome; later to Spain and Portugal, then to France, Germany, Holland, and Britain, finally to countries with very cold and, by inference, invigorating winters exemplified by the United States, Canada, and the U.S.S.R. A parallel could be drawn between the supposedly early maturing of the individual in tropical climates and the early flowering of civilizations in the tropics.

In later years these concepts, attractive as they may be, have been seriously questioned, even completely refuted. A doctor with a long experience in the tropics, especially in Panama and the Philippines, and later practising as well as becoming Professor of Experimental Medicine in the University of Cincinnati is Clarence Mills, whose fascinating book *Climate Makes the Man*, written in 1941–2 was published in England in 1944. Mills combines the evidence of laboratory work on rats and mice with his own tropical experience and observations. Fundamental to his argument is the behaviour of rats kept respectively under cool (65° F. or 18° C.), medium (76° F. or 24° C.), and hot conditions (90–91° F. or 33° C.). Those in the cool chambers develop early both physically and mentally, they are healthy, perpetually hungry, grow rapidly, reach sexual maturity early, and have large healthy families, and are markedly intelligent, e.g. in finding their way through a maze and remembering what they have learnt. In the hot chamber the rats are listless, lack appetite, mature more slowly, and have a markedly lower intelligence but, living tranquil vegetative lives, survive to a ripe old age.

Deaths from pneumonia were almost nil in these controlled conditions compared with 20 per cent. in rats suffering the vagaries of the laboratory conditions outside. On the other hand there was a severe incidence of cancer in the cold-chamber group, the first death occurring at 10 months. In the hot-chamber group not a single case of tumorous growth was found till 15 months had passed. Further, tumours grew twice as fast in the cold chamber. It would seem that cancer of these types is not favoured by tropical conditions.

If the lessons are applied directly to human beings, we may expect those living in the tropics to show, when protected from disease (against which both rats and humans show lessened resistance at high temperatures), the world records for longevity. Expectation of life can no longer be regarded as a test of 'health', and when medical services are fully extended in the tropics, we may expect to see a complete change in the age-structure of the population with ever increasing proportions in the higher age-groups. The resulting social problems relating to the case of old people, already so well known in advanced countries, will surely be added to the other problems already existing in the tropics.

But can man be directly matched in this way with the behaviour of laboratory rats? In the first place it must be pointed out that rats and mice—indeed all laboratory animals—are provided with fur as a protection against cold but are ill-adapted for tropical conditions in lacking adequate means of heat loss. In the absence of body sweat glands rats under tropical conditions develop lengthened tails and other modifications of limited efficiency. Man, on the other hand, would seem to be designed by nature as a tropical animal. He has no protective fur against cold but is provided with abundant and well distributed sweat glands and so probably the most efficient heat-loss mechanism of any animal.

But if we accept at least some parallel between mice and men, where is the familiar idea of early sexual maturity and premature ageing in tropical populations? Mills argues that this is a great fallacy. He contends that in the tropics sexual maturity comes later, and despite the heightening of sexual appetite, which is admitted, and the common laxity in sexual relations, the rate of conception is low. He contends that the restrictive moral codes of dwellers in more temperate lands are an unconscious reaction to the higher rates of conception and the appallingly high birth-rate which would otherwise result.

Early in 1954 the Council on Foreign Relations in the United States set up a Study Group on Climate and Economic Development in the Tropics. In 1957 their report was published as a book with this title, edited by Douglas H. K. Lee, and is a veritable mine of information. A chapter is devoted to Human Health and Efficiency and one is impressed not so much by what is known as by what is not yet known. As to the direct effect of climate, the Study Group concluded:

(a) People who are unaccustomed to the climatic conditions of the tropics experience many direct physiological effects which impair their efficiency, sometimes to the point of clinical disturbance.

(b) With continued experience, the major disturbances tend to disappear in about ten days, although longer periods are required for complete acclimatization (p. 96).

I give a comment on this later. Lee goes on to list
specific psychological disturbances arising in the course

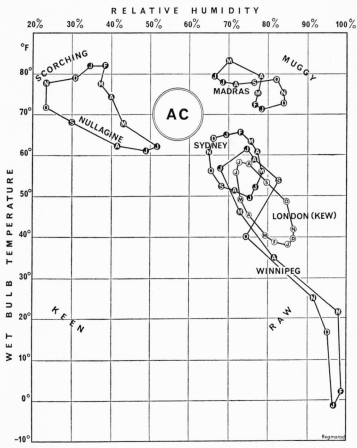

FIG. 15. Climographs of selected stations showing Griffith Taylor's diagrams
to illustrate human comfort. Redrawn from A. A. Miller, with London added
and a circle marked AC representing the approximate range for air-conditioned buildings mentioned in the text.

of exposure to hot conditions: (*a*) some loss of mental
initiative, probably the most important single direct
result; (*b*) accuracy may be noticeably affected in

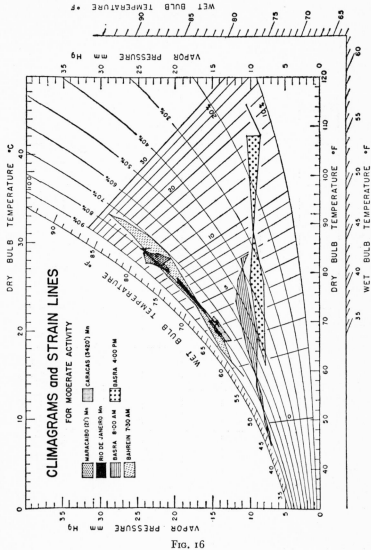

FIG. 16

(For legend see facing page.)

poorly motivated persons; and (c) a person may feel the performance of a given task calls for more concentration. He notes, however, that 'climate is a convenient bogeyman to be blamed for psychological difficulties whose real origin is personal'.

We owe much to Professor Griffith Taylor for developing the idea of 'comfort' where human reactions to climate are concerned. His 'climograph' is a twelve-sided diagram with wet-bulb temperatures as ordinates and relative humidities as abscissae; the twelve average monthly figures are plotted for the localities required. This has been developed into charts of 'Thermal Strain'. In the diagram developed by Lee 'most persons are comfortable only between $3\frac{1}{2}$ and 6 degrees of strain'.

Such diagrams are based essentially on temperature and humidity. The element of air pressure, especially the low pressures at high altitudes, introduces a different element of suspected rather than known importance, exemplified by the high-level living on the plateau of Kenya.

Earlier this year I found myself early one Sunday morning in the crater-harbour of Pago Pago in American Samoa and the scene used by Somerset Maugham for *Rain*, one of the most powerful stories ever written—

FIG. 16. Charts of thermal strain. The development of Griffith Taylor's concepts, following Professor D. H. K. Lee. Professor Lee's directions for using the diagram are as follows: Find the point corresponding to the particular temperature and humidity under consideration; the position of this point relative to the numbered oblique lines indicates the relative strain to be expected in a man doing light work and normally clad, when the rate of air movement is moderate. Most persons are comfortable between $3\frac{1}{2}$ and 6; few are comfortable above or below. Deterioration in muscular performance begins at 12; recommended upper limit for daily work is 14–18; mental performance deteriorates at 30; distress follows at higher levels. The very serious position of the Persian Gulf ports is noteworthy; it is to be recalled that a number of deaths occurred among British troops at Kuwait in 1961.

equally gripping as a play—of the indirect effects of climate on human behaviour. The general theme is well known—the strangely assorted passengers from a steamship marooned for a few days in a ramshackle hotel in the hot steamy atmosphere of around 80° F., saturated air, with tropical rain pounding incessantly on the corrugated iron roof. The efforts of the missionary to win the soul of the prostitute Susie result only in his succumbing to the call of the flesh and his suicide in remorse, his colourless wife but a helpless spectator. Few who have lived in the humid tropics can fail to recognize certain climatic influences: the helpless lethargy engendered by moist heat, yet the heightening of sexual desire; the sense of imprisonment on an island in a sodden world. Mills in his *Climate Makes the Man* repeatedly refers to a 'vegetative' existence, and quotes his own experience in Panama. In pursuing his argument, however, he tends to overemphasize those facts which support his views, and his judgement becomes subjective—for example in his virulent condemnation of coffee.

Realizing this danger of unscientific subjective judgement I hesitate to quote from personal experience. However, I have long been fascinated by this question of direct climatic effects on man—inspired no doubt by reading as a student Ellsworth Huntingdon,[1] L. C. W. Bonacina, and L. W. Lyde[2]—and when appointed to a post in Burma in 1921 I determined to record my observations. In fact I registered (so far as I know I am still registered) as a Ph.D. student in the University of

---

[1] Especially *The Pulse of Asia*, London, 1907.
[2] Notably Bonacina's little book, *Climatic Control*, edited by L. W. Lyde, London, 1911.

London for a thesis to be entitled 'A Statistical Study of the Effects of the Climate of Burma on the Habits of Europeans'. For two years I was engaged in exploring for oil and minerals in the remoter parts of the country and for three further years, whilst based in the University of Rangoon as Professor of Geology and Geography, continued to travel extensively, and had thus unusual opportunities of personal experience. I found, however, in making notes on colleagues, friends, and acquaintances my investigations threatened to become an embarrassingly personal sort of Kinsey Report, and there is such a thing as the law of libel! However, a few points stand out.

The first is the direct effect of heat. The damp heat of Rangoon, with temperatures of 80–85° F. (rarely up to 90°), with relative humidity up to 100 and rarely below 70 or 90, rendered me a constant sufferer from a form of prickly heat which was extremely irritating. In my case it did not produce skin eruptions which could be treated externally; cool or cold baths so heightened the irritation as to be maddening, a really hot bath was tolerable and sometimes soothing, but long periods of sleeplessness at night had an obvious effect on temper, nerves, and efficiency. With the dry heat of central Burma's Dry Zone prickly heat was less marked. There the thermometer would climb every afternoon in the hot season to 104 or 106° F. and with me a definite change took place when air temperature exceeded blood heat. I recall resting in the heat of the afternoon, not sleeping, but in a state of such mental lethargy that the mind became literally a perfect blank.

The second point I would like to emphasize is a view of acclimatization, or acclimation, rather different from the usual quoted above from Lee. The first year I found it normal and natural to carry on with hours of work and with timing, character, and quantity of food and drink to which I had been accustomed at home. I found it difficult to sympathize with colleagues who liked to complete their day's work by noon and fritter away the time which seemed to offer so many opportunities for reading and research. The second year I found myself slipping into local habits, the third year the life lived by my colleagues was seen to be attuned to dictates of local circumstances, but particularly to climate. The natural urge was to follow it. Thus acclimatization is seen as *adapting* one's own living to the environment, rather than 'getting accustomed to the climate'.

It is well known that animals—in laboratory or field or in the wild—show a remarkable instinct in knowing their physiological needs. The wild animals trekking miles to a salt-lick, the cow breaking through the hedge to get at the 'roughage' not available in the lush meadow pasture, are two obvious examples. It has been shown that human infants, given a free selection of foods, will quickly select what constitutes a balanced diet. With adults the old music-hall song made famous by Marie Lloyd—'A little of what you fancy does you good'— enshrines a great truth. Notice it is 'a little' so that indulgence to excess is ruled out, and that is where things have so often gone wrong. In the tropics an intake of fluids which would seem incredible in cold lands is really necessary. There is a lot to be said for the old rule of reserving alcohol till after sunset, and for its use in moderation. That does not condone the imbibing of innumerable 'coasters'—the gin and water of the West Coast of Africa—or 'stingas'—the whisky-sodas of

Malaya and the East, between the first 'sundowner' and dinner some four or five hours later. The White Man's Grave earned its reputation as much by gin as by fever.

What is the significance of the very widespread use of hot or highly spiced foods in the tropics—from the curries of India to the *chile-con-carne* of tropical America? The most likely explanation would seem to be the need to stimulate the digestive juices from a tropical lethagy.

Clothing in the tropics introduces a topic of great interest. The instinct of primitive man is to wear as little as possible and to allow the sweat glands of the body to carry out their function as freely as possible. Such clothing as may be worn is dictated more by concepts of modesty or of adornment than of protection from the elements. In tropical climates, especially those subject to sudden changes, such as heavy rainstorms, there is ample evidence that almost any form of clothing increases liability to illnesses stemming from drying of damp clothes, notably pneumonia. Any European in the tropics soon becomes aware of the dangers of a chill after exercise, with falling temperatures after sundown, and especially from that evil instrument of civilization, the electric fan. In particular, many stomach troubles are to be traced accordingly.

I am old enough to remember the incredible changes of fashion dictated by the medical fraternity for white dwellers in the tropics. Fortunately, by 1921 when I first went to the tropics the red flannel spine-pad, tied by tapes round neck and body, had already gone out, though I was offered one by my London tropical out-fitters. This, of course, protected the spine from the disastrous rays of the sun. The wearing of a sun helmet or solar topee—white, lined green, or pith-helmet of khaki—was *de rigueur*. A double terai, being more elegant, was permitted for the ladies. So insistent were the authorities on protecting the head from the sun that several major companies in the East reserved the right to repatriate instantly any of their white staff who refused to conform. Non-conformity by wives if not grounds for divorce was adequate grounds for compulsory home leave. We were all so indoctrinated with fear of sunstroke—through the skull—that there seemed nothing strange at the time in my photograph of a government colleague swimming in a river pool in central Burma in the nude except for his sun helmet. It was not till 1937 when a large delegation from the British Association invaded a P. & O. liner to attend the 25th Jubilee of the Indian Science Congress that a leading doctor boldly asserted there was no such thing as sunstroke (heat apoplexy was different and real) and walked the deck *without a hat*, later doing the same thing in India. The old hands shook their heads and waited, perhaps a little gleefully, though in vain, for the inevitable collapse and return to England, on a stretcher. The Burma campaign of the Second World War finally killed the sun-helmet except as a status-symbol amongst lesser executives. On the other hand I was looked upon as somewhat peculiar for wearing dark glasses (Crookes) in 1921, and they did not become common till later. Now that one can study browning European bodies on every tropical beach, where a few years ago a hatless human would be scarcely thinkable, and where the native inhabitants still shun the sun, one inevitably wonders. Many know the feeling of lassitude and extreme tiredness after a day's sunbathing. Is that as it should be? Mention is made later of Russian evidence of an increase in skin cancer associated with exposure of the body to the sun's rays.

An old adjustment to life in the tropics is the chair with its long fixed or adjustable arms over which one draped one's legs so that the feet were just above the general level of the body. The swelling of feet and ankles associated with hot weather was thereby reduced or eliminated.

Mills describes in his book the close association between stormy weather and respiratory infections. He gives his criteria for selecting the Los Angeles area for his Cincinnati sufferers from sinusitis but describes how the cooling breezes off the Pacific and daily surf-bathing induced nasal catarrh in all his family which persisted till they returned via the deserts of Arizona. Although he stresses the lowered resistance to infections resulting from residence in the tropics and praises the invigorating effects (at least on most people) of his native Cincinnati (January average at freezing point) he says nothing of the fact that actually most of our lives are spent in artificial climates of our own making.

Within the past few decades an entirely new aspect of the relation between man and climate has assumed a major importance. It is the advent of air-conditioning, combining both heating and cooling, as well as literally the conditioning of air by control of humidity and elimination of impurities in varying degree. Heating of living accommodation is almost as old as man himself: doubtless Stone Age man sat around his fire in his woodland clearings, and certainly cave man, driven to seek shelter with the oncoming of an ice age, both needed and enjoyed a fire in his cave—for warmth as well as for cooking. The Romans had no illusions about the winter chill of Britain and the hot air system of central heating, for their *villae* in this country were models unsurpassed for nearly 2,000 years. It may be claimed that central heating in its modern forms emerged as a defence-response by European migrants faced with the much more severe winters of the North American continent.

In the past, and indeed right to the present, writers on the man–climate relationship seem to ignore or to overlook the large proportion of his life which man spends 'indoors' and so in a climate to a large extent of his own making. In the winter months in the heart of Canada—for example a town dweller in Winnipeg—or the American mid-west, where average temperatures are below freezing, day and night, for long periods on end, the only contact with the natural climate may be a few minutes each day while passing from the centrally-heated flat to the heated car, from the latter to the centrally-heated office or shop, and then the reverse procedure a few hours later. If this daily adventure took place in Japan, the mouth would doubtless be protected by a woollen pad slung from the ears.[1]

As already noted, it has been widely claimed that man is naturally a tropical animal; his body is so nearly hairless as to offer no protection against cold, though well adapted by the distribution of sweat glands to withstand heat. Certainly, *Homo sapiens* variety *americanus* behaves as a tropical animal in the winter months, for American offices and hotels not infrequently maintain a temperature of 25° C. (77° F.) or more. For both men and women the winter woollies of European lands

[1] On the very day this lecture was delivered the Radio Doctor, broadcasting on the Home Service, advocated the use of such masks for bronchial sufferers and described how they could be made.

are unknown; on arrival at the office coats are shed and work proceeds in the normal summer garb of nylon shirts and 'pants' underlain only by briefs. On arrival at a home for an evening's social relaxation the women shed their protective suede knickers as normally as they do their fur coats.

Now the picture is changing. Central heating has become almost standard in Britain in hotels, offices, and public buildings (except perhaps churches) as well as in blocks of flats or apartments and is rapidly invading the individual private home. *Homo sapiens* sub-variety *britannicus* (variety *europeicus* as a whole is nearer *americanus* in habits) tends to retain a superior scepticism where central heating is concerned, and at any rate prefers lower temperatures and is only gradually becoming tolerant of windows which are not intended to open to admit 'fresh air'. In an advertisement in *The Times* in 1962 covering a variety of central heating installations for the private home, stressing the rival merits of solid fuel, gas, oil, and electricity, all recommended by the Heating Centre in London, only seven out of eleven specified the temperature to be maintained. Two allowed for keeping temperatures in bedrooms at 55° F. and in living-rooms at 65° F., another for temperatures between 55° F. and 65° F., a fourth for living-rooms at 65° F., bedrooms 'a little less'. This is scarcely more than 'background' heating and would need to be supplemented by fires in both living-rooms and bedrooms. Another system allowed for radiators to be set thermostatically at 70° F., with the air temperature of the rooms, presumably, considerably less. The remaining two systems, both for solid fuel, allowed for 'house temperature' of 70° F.

In evidence presented to the Study Group on Climate and Economic Development in the Tropics, E. P. Palmater summarized the American view that the interior of a building should maintain a mean daily temperature 5–6° F. above the mean daily temperature outside, that heating is necessary when the outside mean daily temperature falls below 65° F. and cooling when it rises above 70° F., and that limits of 70–75° F. are desirable inside. As the mean daily temperature in the hottest month in the hottest part of Britain is 63° F. (London in August), British buildings should always be heated, except for the occasional rare day in summer.

Personally, I regard home central heating in Britain as an absolute essential, and since one never-to-be-forgotten winter in 1926–7 on returning home from Burma, have not lived in a house without it. I keep a secret black list of friends who, however much I like them and their company, have houses which are unstayable-in. But my central heating is of a hit-and-miss variety—a radiator to be turned off if one feels too hot, a window to be opened if the air outside seems pleasant and balmy. In Britain background central heating is as much a protection against damp (as I find in Cornwall) as against cold, but here again we are hit-and-miss and keep little to any definite figure of relative humidity. After the installation of automatic gas-fired central heating in my old manor-house in Cornwall, parts of which are at least 700 years old, and much of the woodwork at least a century or two, all doors, frames, and floorboards dried, shrank, and in many cases split. All I know, personally, is that I am quite incapable of work, mental or otherwise, if I am sensibly cold.

In November 1962 the British Government became involved in a big way in this question of indoor climate. On 2 November the Offices, Shops, and Railway Premises Bill was introduced into the Commons by the Minister of Labour. Designed to establish minimal conditions of health, safety, and welfare, it affects 8 million workers in over 400,000 premises. Under 'Temperature' it provided that effective measures shall be taken to secure and maintain 'a reasonable temperature' and, where most of the work done does not involve 'severe physical effort', a 'temperature of less than 60 degrees Fahrenheit shall not be deemed after the first hour to be a reasonable temperature while work is going on'. This was in conjunction with a minimum of 400 cubic feet per employee, i.e. a space 8 feet by 5 feet in a room or office 10 feet high. It will be noticed that some of the central-heating plant advertised would not provide this minimum.

From a medical point of view Dr. F. A. Chrenko has recently reviewed the somewhat chaotic present position in two articles entitled 'Human Factors in Heating', published in *Design*, the organ of the Council of Industrial Design (**165**, **166**, 1962, especially pp. 50–53). Contrary to evidence which I present in my next lecture, he is inclined to make light of the significance of ionization.

Although man's fight against excessive heat is probably as old as that against cold, really effective measures are quite modern. The early attempts to counteract oppressive heat were along two lines. One was to set the air in motion. Its temperature is not thereby lowered, but transpiration from the body surface is increased and the body cooled by being brought into contact with fresh supplies of air. The fan, wielded by the individual or better by slaves or other attendants to whom fell the effort needed, is millenia old. The waving to and fro of the punkah of India, activated by a string not infrequently attached to and operated by the big toe of the punkah-wallah, made life tolerable for the European both in his office and in his dining-room at home. In due course it gave place to the electric fan, to which indeed the name punkah was transferred.

The other attack against heat was by house construction, the broad principle being to imprison relatively cool night air to last during the hot hours of the day. Thick walls, shaded verandas, the shutting of windows in the early morning, double roofs with a slow-conducting air blanket, sprinkling of water to cause cooling by evaporation, were all amongst widespread methods.

But, to use a modern expression, the real breakthrough has come with air-conditioning within the last three or four decades. In my own early days in Burma and India, from 1921 onwards, we purchased ice and put it into an ice-box to keep drinks cold. At that date the Pullman cars on American railways were cooled by passing air over large blocks of ice, the ice replenished at intervals. Refrigerators for food were beginning to come into general use where electricity was available, and curiously enough one of the earliest examples of air-conditioning in the tropics I remember was in 1934 in the dining-room of the Emir of Kano's palace in northern Nigeria, where a huge refrigerator, quite empty, doors open and lights on, was part of the furniture of the royal dining-room. It seemed laughable to us then, but the idea was in advance of the times.

Early air-conditioning was a toy and was overdone. In the late twenties my late sister-in-law, Lady Stamp, attending a play in an air-conditioned New York theatre, contracted pneumonia and spent some weeks in hospital. In 1933 the train south to Florida was cooled to under 60° F. (16° C.) and I was glad to have at hand my winter overcoat while I ate in the dining-car. One of the early commercial attempts at air-conditioning I remember in India was the dining-room of the Taj Mahal Hotel in Bombay. Fine! Business executives could relax over luncheon and enjoy a couple of Martinis, but the result on afternoon work in their offices at 90° F. was disastrous and the hotel was forced to probe into the loss of many regular lunchers.

The realization has, of course, come that what may be called 'casual' air-conditioning of this sort must not involve a difference of more than ten degrees Fahrenheit from outdoor to indoor temperatures.

But we come now to the modern phase of air-conditioning, whereby with a single plant an enclosed area, e.g. a large building, may be supplied with air heated in winter, cooled in summer, with a controlled relative humidity, with the air washed of physical impurities and to a less but major extent of chemical impurities. It is a *sine qua non* that the space is enclosed, i.e. it would be upset by open windows or doors connecting with the outside world. In a few words, men working in such a building are working in pure or at least purified air in a definite climate which man himself has selected as the ideal—we may presume because it is pleasant, healthy, and conducive to maximum output and efficiency. Let us select a few examples of these man-made ideal climates.

It is claimed that the new Shell Centre in London—officially the 'Shell Centre which houses the London components of the central office of the Royal Dutch Shell Group of Companies'—finished in 1962 but not yet fully occupied at the time of writing (October 1962), is the largest office building in Britain, and may lay claim to being the largest in Europe. The main tower block rises to 351 feet above street level in 27 storeys; the total cubic capacity of the building is 28,400,000 cubic feet and floor space 1,872,000 square feet. It is designed to accommodate 5,000 people who, since restaurant and canteen facilities are provided, will spend the whole of their working days, or let us say 25 per cent. of their working lives, in climatic conditions deliberately selected. The whole is completely air-conditioned. The heat range is between 68 and 74° F. (20–24° C.), individual offices being able to control their temperatures between these figures in the winter, whilst in summer the system is under cooling load. Relative humidity is maintained between 40 and 60. It is difficult to match this 'climate' among the natural climates of the world, because it is equable and the relative humidity is low. It might prove detrimental to health because of its monotony if the people concerned were living in it for the *whole* of their time instead of a third of each day. It may be called sub-tropical, oceanic (because of equability), but dry. A fairly close approximation is offered by leeward regions in Hawaii (74° F. annual average), so Shell employees can think of themselves as permanently on the beach at Waikiki. The movement of the air there afforded by the trade winds is supplied by the constantly changing air, and fluorescent lighting replaces sunshine. Incidentally, this fundamental change in British habits is certain to have wide repercussions. American men and women wear the same underclothing as well as the same weight indoor outer clothing throughout the year. The old British customs of changing into 'winter woollies' and 'ne'er casting a clout till May be out' seem destined to disappear with a consequent change in demand which will seriously affect manufacturers. It is significant that the first high executive I visited in his Shell office—in November—was in his shirtsleeves, and I soon found myself apologizing for removing my waistcoat.

A second example of complete air-conditioning I will take from the luxury liner *Monterey* of the American Matson Line, plying across the Pacific from San Francisco to Auckland, New Zealand, and in which I travelled in March 1962 from Auckland via Fiji, Pago Pago, and Honolulu to San Francisco. Climatically this was from New Zealand in autumn, across the equatorial doldrums, trade wind Hawaii to San Francisco in draughty March. Double doors cut off all deck space from the public rooms, dining saloon, passages, and state-rooms—i.e. the whole 'living part' of the ship is enclosed and kept closely to 72° F., with a range roughly of 70–74° F. and a relative humidity of 60–65. Passengers have a 'blower' control in their cabins to regulate the intake and temperature of air over a considerably wider range. There is no doubt of the pleasant effect of the temperature: it was strange that on going out on deck we never knew whether it would be hotter or colder. Such conditions of sea-travel were scarcely in mind when doctors prescribed a 'long sea voyage' for convalescents.

As a third example I go to Hong Kong. On the margin

of the monsoon tropics, the climate of Hong Kong's main settlement, Victoria, is given in the following figures:

TABLE II

	Temperature		Rainfall	
	° F.	° C.	in.	mm.
January	60	15·5	1·0	25
February	58	14	1·3	33
March	63	17	3·3	84
April	70	21	5·4	137
May	77	25	12·4	315
June	87	27	16·3	414
July	82	28	15·9	404
August	81	27	14·8	376
September	80	27	12·5	317
October	76	23	5·2	132
November	69	21	1·4	36
December	63	17	1·0	25
Average	72	22	..	..
Range	24	14	..	..
Total	..	..	90·5	2298

In the summer rainy season humidity is constantly high, one lives in a steam bath. However efficient the fans, however frequently one replaces evaporation losses by iced drinks, the climate at this season must be admitted as exhausting—or at least failing to conduce to maximum physical and mental output. An experiment was made of installing air-conditioning in the university library. Reading hours by students jumped 30 per cent.—a lot, for the Chinese are assiduous readers even in most difficult circumstances. But it is not perhaps fully realized that the artificial climate now commonly used in the larger factories of Hong Kong has made possible the spectacular economic development of the past decade. A good example is high quality printing, which Hong Kong now does for the European market; with controlled temperature and moisture paper does not stretch in the course of the work. Similarly, handling of fine fabrics is no longer subject to the old dangers of contamination by human sweat.

During one of my recent visits to Hong Kong I had the opportunity of discussing the problem with Mr. Wilfred Wong of the American Engineering Corporation, who has carried out the air-conditioning of many new buildings there. He quoted the standard derived from those set by the United States Department of Agriculture, 1941, of 70° F. and 50 or less relative humidity. Since American standards for winter heating are 75–80° F., it seems incongruous to set an indoor temperature almost ten degrees less in summer than in winter. Certainly these levels are regarded as too low in Hong Kong. With average summer temperatures (June–September inclusive) of 78–80° F. (26° C.) but liable to rise during the day to a maximum of 92° F. (34° C.) and humidity 70–90 per cent., it is found that the thermostatic control is best set at 76° F., i.e. at that temperature outside the system begins to function and reduces inside temperature to 75° F. (24° C.), with relative humidity 55. In winter a desirable indoor temperature is regarded as 70° F. (21–22° C.) with relative humidity 55 when outdoor temperatures average 58° F. or about 14° C. (February). The new university library is air-conditioned to these standards. Since Hong Kong is not atypical of large areas on the margins of the wetter tropics, experience suggests that human efficiency is well served by a temperature of 70–75° F. (21–24° C.) and a relative humidity of 55.

To bring the story right up to date, history is being made at this moment in that, less than a mile away, what claims to be the first completely air-conditioned block of flats in Britain is nearing completion. I refer to Bilton Towers in Great Cumberland Place—conveniently located, some sceptics might claim, a few blocks from Harley Street. There is now the possibility of a Shell executive occupying one of these flats and so spending, say, 90 per cent. of his (or her) life in an artificial climate deliberately chosen.

But these conditions of living have already been reached under very different circumstances in the dry south-western states of U.S.A.—e.g. in Arizona. Since air-conditioning in the home and office has entirely eliminated the danger of debilitating heat, American manufacturers are appreciating the great advantage of urban development in these arid lands. Towns, dependent mainly on industry, are growing three times as rapidly as in the United States as a whole. For the family man the expenditure on winter heating, so heavy in the north-east, is almost nil, free open air life with plenty of sunshine the year round and a minimum of clothing for the children, an irrigated garden to delight with flowers the year round instead of days and weeks of winter snow-clearing, it is little wonder that workers are willing to accept lower wages than in the winter-cold lands. This pointer indicates clearly a possible future for many of the world's hot deserts where water, being scarce, is more effectively used in providing the needs of a town of 100,000 inhabitants than satisfying the requirements of a few thousand farmers.

A few years ago I was involved in a discussion with a number of vice-chancellors of universities in West Pakistan, where July *averages* are over 90° F. or 32° C. The proposal was to build a completely air-conditioned university, within which the students would live and work and play for the nine or ten months of the university year without going outside other than very occasionally. What should be the ideal climate? A seasonal rhythm? A daily rhythm? Attuned to the outside world or quite independent? I am far from satisfied that we yet have the full answers.

3

THE MAPPING OF MORTALITY AND MORBIDITY

A MAP may be an end in itself, designed to show the essential features of a country or district, independent of the uses which may be made of it, though drawn mindful of the range and varied interests of its likely users. This is broadly true of the maps in a world atlas: they serve as works of reference where we may find the location of a country or a place in the news, where we may check the route of our proposed continental holiday, where we may try to visualize the type of country and the boundaries of a new African republic. The maps published on various scales by the Ordnance Survey in Britain are general purpose maps: the larger scales interest the landowner, his surveyor, and the dealer in property; the medium scales, such as the 1:25,000 (2½ inches to the mile) not only are of greatest service to the walker but serve as a training ground in map-reading in the schools. Smaller scales serve the motorist, as well as depicting to the general inquirer the general lie of the land.

Very frequently a map is designed or modified to serve the needs of groups of users. Maps for the motorist include classification and numbering of roads, often show distances between towns, and may have insets of complex town areas. The world is covered by a series of 1:1,000,000 maps for the use of air pilots, the seas are charted with emphasis on depths, but very little detail of the lands, for the use of mariners. Maps of land use and vegetation serve not only the specialist's needs but are of general interest because all citizens have an interest in their country and how its resources are used. Very frequently maps for general use have a bias in one direction or another. The relief of the land, the position of its mountains, hills, valleys, and plains, is so fundamental that school atlases and such great works as *The Times Atlas* have basically physical maps—i.e. maps coloured to show relief. The older tradition was to emphasize political geography by adopting different colours for different countries. Our own Ordnance Survey owes its initiation as well as the name it still bears to the need for maps should Napoleon Bonaparte have actually invaded Britain as he planned to do, and the maps still emphasize features of major significance to armies in the field.

But we are concerned in this lecture with maps of a rather different character. Though constructed primarily to show facts, to show distributions with an accuracy which cannot be attained in pages of description or statistics, and in such a way as to emphasize patterns, their prime importance is as research tools. Any craftsman appreciates the significance of having the right tools for the job; any research worker will appreciate the care and thought which must go into the preparation of his apparatus; a computer which has taken years to design and to construct may do its really vital work in a matter of minutes. It is much the same with maps used as research tools. There may be a dozen different ways of showing the same facts: only one will bring out some difference in distribution which may be the signpost to a major discovery.

In comparison with the enormous costs in these days of so many of our research programmes, it is surely worth while that far more attention should be paid to the relatively simple and inexpensive, though often laborious and time consuming, work of cartographical analysis.

In my first lecture some examples of world and continental maps were given. They show the broad picture of disease distribution and suggest limitation of many diseases to certain broad climatic belts or large geographical regions. We may now look in some more detail at the work of mapping on the national level and take as an example England and Wales.

The Registrar-General collects and publishes annual statistics of births and deaths. Deaths are recorded according to an internationally agreed classification, they are attributed to the last home address of the patient, not to the hospital or institution, which would give an undue prominence to towns. Sources of error exist—in wrong diagnosis, for example—but on the whole our statistics are undoubtedly amongst the world's most accurate. Comparison with the past over long periods may break down because of changed classification, but we may safely use the figures for any given year or over short periods. Moreover, the figures are available for small administrative areas—rural districts, urban districts, and the towns of the country of higher rank. It is possible to get a general picture by simply using the county and county borough figures: a more accurate one by using the smaller units.

Obviously, there are considerable differences in the age-composition of the population in different districts. There are the thriving industrial towns pulsating with young life; there are the Bournemouths and Cheltenhams to which many retire to end their days and which accordingly have a large percentage of their total population in the higher age-groups and a correspondingly high death-rate. Consequently, a map showing the crude death rate emphasizes these differences. Maps showing crude death-rates from any given disease would reflect this overall position; it is therefore necessary to use adjusted death-rates, which the Registrar-General's statistics in fact give. If then for any given disease the mortality over the whole country is taken as 100, it is possible to show where the incidence of the disease is higher or lower. Again one can get the broad picture by using the county as a unit, a more exact picture by taking the smaller administrative units.

A pioneer in the preparation of maps based on the Registrar-General's statistics has been Dr. G. Melvyn Howe of the Department of Geography of University College, Aberystwyth. He dealt in the first place with Wales and some of his maps refer to different types of cancer, separating male and female victims. It is no criticism of Dr. Howe's maps that they raise more questions than they answer. The point is that they all show quite extraordinary variations in the incidence of mortality from named causes. They are factual. We should not rest until we have obtained a satisfactory answer to the question: Why these differences?

Dr. Howe (1959, 1960) has proceeded to the next stage by examining four possible factors—atmospheric pollution, nature of water supply, soils, and blood groups. He concludes:

The pattern of distribution of mortality from lung-bronchus cancer in males is the only one which offers sufficient correlation

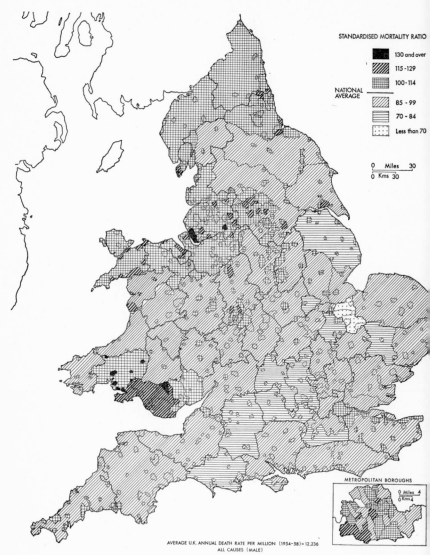

STANDARDISED MORTALITY RATIO

■	130 and over
	115-129
	100-114
NATIONAL AVERAGE	
	85-99
	70-84
	Less than 70

0 Miles 30
0 Kms 30

METROPOLITAN BOROUGHS

0 Miles 4
0 Kms 4

AVERAGE U.K. ANNUAL DEATH RATE PER MILLION (1954-58) = 12,236
ALL CAUSES (MALE)

FIG. 17. Mortality from all causes in England and Wales, 1954–8.
[Howe (1963), *National Atlas of Disease Mortality*, London.]

with the pattern of selected indices of atmospheric pollution to suggest an association with atmospheric carcinogens . . . in the causation of stomach cancer the untreated acidic water-supplies in daily use in the countryside, and in particular those waters polluted by effluent from spoil mounds of defunct lead, zinc, and copper mines . . . might be worthy of further study.

In other words, results to date may be negative, but there are endless possibilities.

We owe to Lord Nathan, during his Presidency of the Royal Geographical Society, the comprehensive project to extend the work of mapping disease distribution to cover the whole of the United Kingdom and to prepare and publish a National Atlas of Disease Mortality—the first of its kind for the country as a whole. A joint committee of the Royal Geographical Society and the British Medical Association was set up and funds were provided by the Wolfson Foundation for a small team of workers under Dr. Howe, with Prof. Cochrane to check and advise from the medical angle. The series of maps was completed in 1962 and the *Atlas*, with descriptive text to each map, published in October 1963.

The statistics used are those for 1954–8. An average of 592,846 persons died annually in those five years—483,257 in England, 61,558 in Scotland, 32,887 in Wales, and 15,144 in Northern Ireland. Of these totals 304,573 were males, 288,273 were females. The average annual death-rate was 12·236 per thousand for males, 10·727 for females.

The *Atlas* includes, in each case for the United Kingdom by Rural Districts, Urban Districts, Metropolitan and County Boroughs, maps of population density, mortality from all causes, and then 14 maps of leading causes of death. There are four maps for cancer (lung, stomach, breast, and uterus), two for diseases of the circulatory system (arteriosclerotic heart disease including coronary disease, and vascular lesions), three for diseases of the respiratory system (bronchitis, pneu-

TABLE III

United Kingdom, 1954–8
Annual Average

Total deaths	Total 592,846	M. 304,573	F. 288,273
Cancer (carcinoma, sarcoma):	107,359	..	..
of trachea, lung, bronchus	..	17,346	2,973
of stomach . . .	..	9,036	7,175
of breast	..	..	9,578
of uterus . . .	..	..	4,492
leukaemia and aleukaemia .	..	1,415	1,191
Circulatory system:			
Arteriosclerotic heart disease	86,019	53,806	32,213
Vascular lesions affecting the central nervous system .	85,956	35,711	50,245
Respiratory system:			
Bronchitis . . .	30,630	20,833	9,797
Pneumonia . . .	25,013	12,740	12,273
Tuberculosis . . .	6,171	4,387	1,784
Digestive system:			
Stomach and duodenal ulcers	5,989	4,286	1,703
Miscellaneous:			
Infant mortality (under 1 year) . .	22,689	..	..
Childbirth . . .	485	..	485
Diabetes mellitus . .	3,783	1,261	2,522
Accidents . . .	18,890	11,261	7,629
Suicides . . .	5,610	3,430	2,180
Other causes . . .	194,252	129,061	142,033

monia, tuberculosis), one for diseases of the digestive system (gastric and duodenal ulcer), and four maps for 'miscellaneous' causes of death. The annexed tables show that the causes mapped account for rather over two-thirds of all deaths. As explained in the Introduction, the purpose of the *Atlas* is:

to show the spatial patterns of variations in disease mortality. Irregularities and anomalies may suggest an association with . . . some climatic factor, with water-supply, atmospheric pollution, type of soil, or micro-organisms and their vectors . . . distribution may reflect the habits, the tempo, the mental tensions and the anxieties of our existence, our diet, or sedentary nature of our work . . . predisposition may be due to heredity. . . .

TABLE IV

United Kingdom

The Changing Character of Mortality

	c. 1900	1954–5	1961
	per cent.	per cent.	per cent.
Cancer	4·5	18·1	18·0
Circulatory system:			
Arteriosclerotic heart disease . .	12·8	14·5	26·9
Vascular lesions	7·0	14·5	14·1
Respiratory system:			
Bronchitis	9·2	5·2	5·5
Pneumonia	7·5	4·2	5·2
Tuberculosis	10·4	1·1	0·6
Digestive system:			
Ulcers	0·3	1·0	0·8
Miscellaneous:			
Infant mortality	23·5	3·8	1·9
Childbirth	0·5	0·1	0·05
Diabetes mellitus	—	0·6	0·7
Accidents	} 3·1	3·2	} 4·2
Suicides		0·9	
Other causes	21·2	32·8	22·05

But the *Atlas* makes no attempt to demonstrate any such possible correlations. It very wisely, at this stage, provides the factual material on which future work may be based.

Elsewhere Dr. Howe (1961) has allowed himself the luxury of some speculation. Dealing with England and Wales he uses the well-known distinction between Highland Britain and Lowland Britain. The latter is distinctly healthier: if you want the maximum chance

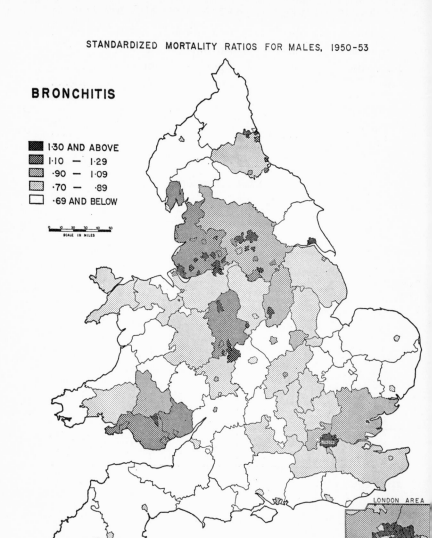

BRONCHITIS

■	1·30 AND ABOVE
▓	1·10 — 1·29
▒	·90 — 1·09
░	·70 — ·89
□	·69 AND BELOW

SCALE IN MILES

LONDON AREA

FIG. 18. Deaths from bronchitis (males) in England and Wales, 1950–3, shown by counties and county boroughs.

[Murray, M. (1962), *Ann. Ass. Amer. Geographers*, **52**, 130.]

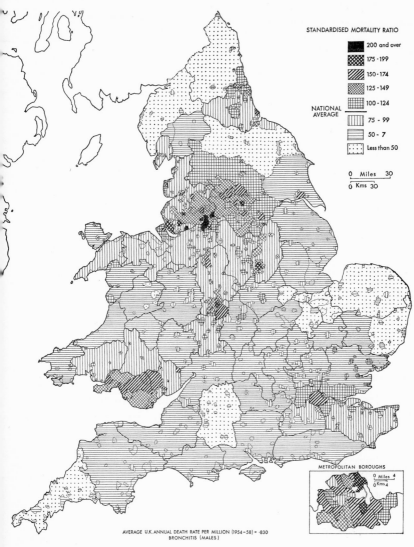

STANDARDISED MORTALITY RATIO

- 200 and over
- 175 - 199
- 150 - 174
- 125 - 149
- 100 - 124

NATIONAL AVERAGE

- 75 - 99
- 50 - 7
- Less than 50

0 Miles 30

0 Kms 30

METROPOLITAN BOROUGHS

0 Miles 4

0 Kms 4

AVERAGE U.K. ANNUAL DEATH RATE PER MILLION (1954–58) = ·830
BRONCHITIS (MALES)

FIG. 19. Deaths from bronchitis in England and Wales, 1954–8. This shows the effect of using smaller administrative divisions than in Fig. 18; the pitfalls are explained in the text.

[Howe (1963), *National Atlas of Disease Mortality*, London.]

of dying, then reside either in one of the remoter Welsh counties or in a northern town!

In the meantime an American worker, Dr. Malcolm Murray of Miami University, Ohio, who spent the academic session of 1958–9 and the summer of 1960 in Britain studying independently in the Registrar-General's Office, has published a very interesting paper entitled 'The Geography of Death in England and Wales' (*Annals of the Association of American Geographers*, **52**, June 1962, 130–49). He gives one map based on the smaller administrative divisions of deaths, male and female, from all causes, for the period 1948–57. We can pick out at once two types of area where death-rates are well above the national average. First, all the older industrial areas—the towns of Lancashire, the West Riding, and the mining valleys of South Wales, Tyneside, and the industrial north-east. These are all areas with unhappy legacies from the industrial revolution in obsolete housing and slums. Some more isolated towns also stand out on the map—Hull, Barrow-in-Furness, parts of the Potteries, Black Country, and East End of London are examples. The second type of area with a bad record is the remote and poor rural areas notably in north and west Wales, the Pennines, and Lakes. Indeed, the map almost divides itself into the familiar two-fold division of Highland Britain and Lowland Britain as Howe has independently noted. The areas with the best records are the lowland farming areas, especially those distinguished by having the better soils and the most developed farming techniques—the prosperous farming areas, in other words.

Dr. Murray then gives a series of maps showing deaths, all for males, for the period 1950–3 on the simplified basis of counties and county boroughs. His maps thus refer to a period of four years immediately before the five-year period used in the Royal Geographical Society *Atlas*. His map of the so-called English disease—bronchitis—leaves no doubt whatsoever that it is the disease of the towns and cities. Even where incidence is low it increases as one enters the city from the surrounding countryside, as seen with Plymouth, Exeter, Bristol, Southampton, Brighton, Ipswich, Norwich, Northampton, and a host of others—especially sharp in Hull. Where incidence is high, as in Lancashire, Staffordshire, and South Wales, it is at once higher in the towns. The association with smoke and air pollution is inevitable, a question I shall examine in my next lecture.

To a considerable extent pneumonia follows the same pattern: it is a disease of the towns. Upland Wales, with its raw climate and with a bad record in other directions, shows up favourably. By way of contrast tuberculosis of the respiratory system is a disease both of the towns and of the uplands which constitute Highland Britain. Stomach cancer is also markedly prevalent in Highland Britain, especially rural Wales, and has quite a different distribution from lung cancer—a town disease. Curiously, arteriosclerotic heart disease is not particularly marked in towns compared with the country, but seems more prevalent in northern England. Vascular lesions affecting the central nervous system are also marked in Highland Britain. Infant mortality is also higher there.

Even these simple maps show the great variations in distribution pattern, but at once raise questions. On the whole they reflect standard of living; the older industrial areas and the poorer counties alike stand out.

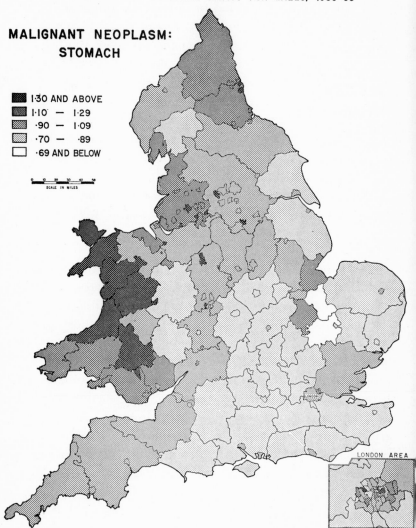

FIG. 20. Deaths from stomach cancer (males) in England and Wales, 1950–3, by counties and county boroughs. This map, by the strong contrasts which it brings out, indicates the existence of major problems of distribution.

[Murray, M. (1962), *Ann. Ass. Amer. Geographers*, **52**, 130.]

Availability of expert medical skill may be a factor in the latter case. The temptation to suggest a correlation with upland areas of poor soil and indifferent climate is great, but the connexion is probably indirect through social and living conditions.

In my first lecture I showed a number of slides, reproduced here as Figs. 3-9, of *world* distribution of diseases and I commented that these could only give a general background picture. At the opposite end of the scale I showed a redrawn version of Dr. John Snow's map of cholera deaths in the Soho district of London in 1848 on which each dot represented one death—a very exact measure (Fig. 10).

Between the two come Dr. Howe's maps of cancer incidence in Wales, the large series of maps he has prepared for the Royal Geographical Society's *National Atlas of Disease Mortality*, and Dr. Murray's maps of England and Wales. All these are what geographers would call 'density' maps. They show the facts by administrative divisions—the county in some cases, smaller units in others. As every geographer knows, there are inherent difficulties in such maps and they may very easily be misleading.

In the first place they show the number of deaths from a given disease, expressed in terms related to total deaths and total population. If the total population and therefore the number of deaths in a given area, say a county like Radnorshire with only 20,000 people or even Herefordshire with 125,000, is small, a half-dozen deaths are liable to make a great difference to the county's ranking and to emphasize unduly the contrast between it and its neighbours. The same is true if the total number of deaths from a given disease is small: a county

with no deaths might appear very favoured, a neighbourhood with two or three deaths might appear as a black
spot.

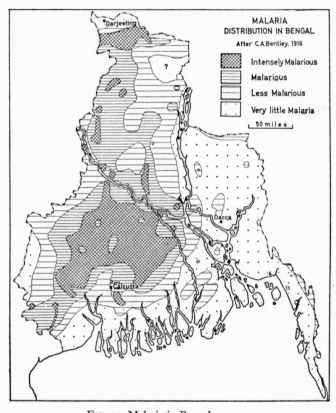

FIG. 21. Malaria in Bengal, *c.* 1910.
[Learmonth, A. T. A. (1957), *Trans. Inst. Brit. Geographers,* **23**, 37. After
Bentley.]

For these reasons all such density maps must be read
with great caution: the differences they show at first
sight may not be statistically significant. The maps
need to be studied side by side with the relevant
statistics and it is often of advantage to use the ordinary

crude 'dot' method of representation—where each dot indicates a certain number of deaths—on another map as a corrective.

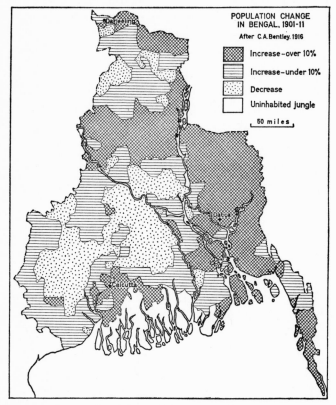

FIG. 22. Rural depopulation of Bengal, 1901–11.
[Learmonth, A. T. A. (1957), *Trans. Inst. Brit. Geographers* (1957), **23**, 37. After Bentley.]

The long-continued work of the Indian Medical Service is a saga of devotion to great ideals. The same may be said of other Indian services and one result is that there exists a body of factual and statistical material in many fields extending over a long period of time.

Important pioneer work in the field of medical geography has been possible and some results of first-class importance have been obtained. Sir Ronald Ross himself was not only born in India but spent there the formative years of his life from 1881 to 1899, retiring as a humble Major of the I.M.S. a short while after he had solved the riddle of the lifecycle of the malarial parasite. Doctors in India have long been puzzled by the irregular distribution of malaria in the subcontinent and as long ago as 1911 Dr. S. R. Christophers studied and mapped the incidence of the epidemic in the Punjab. A few years later Dr. C. A. Bentley used a method of computation suggested by Sir Ronald Ross and illustrated his memoir on *Malaria in Bengal* by an excellent map (Fig. 21). Bengal is a vast alluvial plain, the combined deltas of the Ganges and Brahmaputra. In the course of time the main outlets of the rivers have shifted from west to east so that West Bengal—now part of the state of India of that name—is well described as a land of dead and dying rivers. There are innumerable 'cut-offs' or 'oxbows' of stagnant water in addition to marshes. This is ideal country for *Anopheles* to breed. Similar conditions are spreading, though less prevalent, in the central part of the delta now in Pakistan, whereas in the east there are annual floods, the water finds its way to the sea, and the delta is still being built up. Plenty of water here, but it is not stagnant and, as the map shows, the mosquitoes do not like it and the area is almost free from malaria. The second map (Fig. 22) shows population changes in Bengal in the census decade 1901–11. It leaves no doubt that the people were being killed off or driven out by malaria. Similar abandonment of land through heavy incidence of malaria has been demonstrated elsewhere, notably in Ceylon. With the modern control measures available much rich land, previously abandoned, may become available for resettlement.

In 1926 Dr. S. R. Christophers and Dr. J. A. Sinton

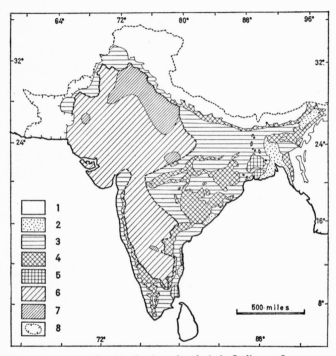

FIG. 23. The distribution of malaria in India, 1938.

1. Areas over 5,000 feet (non-malarious).
2. Known healthy plains.
3. Moderate to high endemicity of more or less static character.
4. Hyper-endemicity of wet hilly tracts and *terai* land.
5. Probably hyper-endemic hill areas.
6. Hyper-endemicity other than hill areas.
7. Variable endemicity associated with dry tracts, much affected by irrigation.
8. Known areas liable to fulminant epidemicity.

The heavy pecked line marks the broad division between the epidemic and endemic regions.

[Learmonth, A. T. A. (1957), *Trans. Inst. Brit. Geographers*, **23**, 37. After Christophers and Sinton.]

prepared what has well been described as a classic map
of malaria in India. As later modified by the Public
Health Commissioner with the Government of India as
applying to 1938, it is shown in Fig. 23. In part of

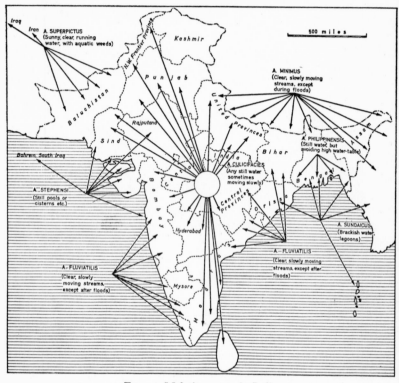

FIG. 24. Malaria vectors in India.
[Learmonth, A. T. A. (1957), *Trans. Inst. Brit. Geographers*, **23**, 37. After Covell.]

India-Pakistan malaria is endemic, in part epidemic, as
shown on the map. Fig. 24 shows that several different
mosquitoes play important roles as vectors. To a considerable extent these maps are now mainly of historic
interest because of the widespread effect of the anti-
malarial campaign using DDT, but they illustrate con-

ditions still prevalent elsewhere. In particular it should be noted that investigations in India left no doubt of the serious part played by new irrigation canals in spreading malaria—a warning not yet fully appreciated elsewhere.

Following on these pioneer studies Arthur Geddes showed how closely population changes in India could be linked with disease conditions. Interest in Indian problems has been revived and quickened by the important studies of Professor A. T. A. Learmonth, especially in Mysore. Dr. Learmonth has pointed out that the main vector of malaria in the Punjab is *Anopheles culicifacies*, which is a fastidious fly. It will breed only in clean water, not in muddy water or water heavily polluted with sewage or tillage. The purification of surface water-supplies clearly does not provide the answer.

As Professor of Medicine in Singapore and later Vice-Chancellor of the University of Malaya, Sir George Allen has a wide experience of health and disease under equatorial conditions in both peace and war—including Japanese p.o.w. camps. In conversation he has mentioned to me that he lectured on the geographical conditions controlling disease distribution at least thirty years ago. One observation of particular interest is that the life cycles of disease organisms in the tropics are often, indeed usually, very complex. Malaria is a good example. It follows that physical conditions must be right for organism, its vectors, and perhaps more than one intermediate host, with man himself offering a low resistance. It follows that where conditions are unsuitable for any one stage the cycle is broken, and one has a clue here to some irregular patchy distributions. I have emphasized elsewhere the curiously discontinuous

incidence of malaria in Burma and the spasmodic occurrence of the relatively innocuous Rangoon fever. It
also follows that wholly satisfactory results in disease
control may be achieved by breaking the cycle at any
one point. To destroy every *Anopheles* is not necessarily
the only way to eradicate malaria.

So far we have been considering mortality. In Britain
a death must be notified and registered pursuant to the
Births and Deaths Registration Act, 1953 (and earlier
Acts). The 'Certified Copy of an Entry of Death' gives
date and place of death, name, sex, and age of deceased,
occupation and residence, and cause of death as certified
by the medical officer concerned. Since a classification
of causes of death is laid down, the only source of error
is in diagnosis.

But mortality is only one part of the story. More
important in the social and economic life of a people is
illness. How far is it possible to go in the mapping of
morbidity or illness, and so in the correlation of good
and bad health with environmental conditions? The
immediate answer is: not very far. A few contagious
diseases are notifiable and where statistics exist they
can be mapped. But of the vast majority of ills which
cause loss of working days, which mean so much in
the happiness of our lives, the records remain in the
physicians' notebooks and files. It may be averred that
some never even get that degree of record. I am convinced that it is here that the need for a new look exists.
Might not the doctor himself get many a surprise if he
kept a wall-map of his district and stuck in coloured
flags for his patients? Now that, in most areas, the vast
majority of patients are treated under the National
Health Service, surely it should not be beyond our

scope to organize a comprehensive recording and mapping of disease morbidity. As a start the mapping of notified cases of scarlet fever, dysentery, acute poliomyelitis, respiratory tuberculosis, whooping cough, and measles should yield results far more significant than the relatively small numbers of deaths from these causes. It seems axiomatic that the small numbers of cases of diphtheria, typhoid, paratyphoid, and encephalitis should automatically be recorded cartographically as they occur. Such records might well prove of decisive value in trying to answer that insistent question—Why?

4

THE WAY AHEAD

To a scientist it is one of the tragedies of advancing years that he sees ahead a vast field of work waiting to be done but with the knowledge that neither time nor opportunity will permit its being done by him. He is left with the hope that he may be permitted to point the way and that others will follow. To my mind the no-man's-land which we broadly call medical geography is a fertile field waiting to be tilled. So far we have only scratched the surface in a few places: future cultivation will yield results of great importance to mankind. Of that I am convinced myself; I shall be happy if I have persuaded in these four lectures some to share my conviction. Before going further let me say that much of the spade work is simply the arduous gathering of precise facts: much is already existing though hidden and unavailable in the general practitioner's notebooks and files, much can be handled and made available by the geographically-minded worker with only limited time and average skill.

Strange as it may seem, we know more about the effects of local differences in climate on the life and well-being of fruit trees than we do of their effect on the life and well-being of human beings. Not many apple-farmers today would risk the expenditure of capital needed to establish an orchard without a careful investigation of soil and climate—probably by calling for expert advice such as that available from my good friend Dr. Basil Furneaux. The fruit farmer has known for long such limitations as a maximum rainfall for Cox's, but a major advance was the realization—applied to fruit farming by Raymond Bush in his book *Frost and the Fruit Grower* (1945)—that cold air behaves much as cold water. It drains downhill, especially down valleys, is easily held up by an obstruction such as a belt of trees or high hedge and is 'ponded back' to form a lake of cold air which is a frost pocket in winter or, more significantly, in blossom-time, when the fruit is setting. Even cutting away a few trees to encourage a free flow of air may make the difference between failure and fortune, just as a few degrees' slope towards the north may so retard the adventurous tree from anticipating the spring that the danger of a late frost is successfully overcome and the year's success is not nipped in the bud.

Yet how many householders, choosing a plot on which to build a home and rear a family, bother to make any such investigation at all? Worse still, how many local authorities seek expert advice on such matters before siting a housing estate? Yet how often have we seen cold, damp fog lying over some tract of land, persisting into daylight hours long after neighbouring areas are clear and bathed in sunshine. Obviously, this *must* affect the health and well-being of the two groups of inhabitants.

After a lapse of a century or so we are beginning to take up these matters seriously. I say deliberately after a century because I am reminded of the pioneer efforts of Dr. Alfred Haviland who produced in 1882 a 'Health-guide Map for Brighton' and in the following year a similar map of Scarborough. There was then a lively interest in 'spas' and 'watering places' and the maps on the large scale of 9 inches to 1 mile stressed in particular 'aspect'. Professor Gilbert in his 1958 paper already quoted has recently redirected attention to these pioneer maps. So great was the interest of our Victorian ancestors in their search for curative 'waters' and 'bracing air' or other climatic conditions able to ameliorate ills which the physicians of the day could not, that when Ventnor on the sheltered, sunny, south-facing shore of the Isle of Wight was rightly lauded as having such desirable features, the price of land is said to have shot up four or five times in as many weeks.

Considering Great Britain as a whole, the sun shines on an average throughout the year from rather less than 3 hours a day—25 per cent. of the possible—as in the north of Scotland and the neighbourhood of Manchester to a little over 5 hours—42 per cent. of the possible—in a few favoured localities along the south coast. Consequently Britons appreciate the sun, and expressions such as 'living on the sunny side of the street' or 'having a place in the sun' have become synonymous with a concept of affluence and well-being. Yet in practice extraordinarily little serious attention is paid to insolation, its measurement, its relation to health, and its significance in the siting of houses. Professor Alice Garnett of the University of Sheffield published her pioneer study on *Insolation and Relief* as long ago as 1937 and in it worked out principles from Alpine examples which she has since applied to conditions in this country, especially in those areas of deep valleys and steep slopes such as surround Sheffield. In Britain the sun only rises about 15 degrees above the horizon at noon in midwinter and it is possible, indeed quite common, for a valley side to have no direct sunshine in winter months, whereas the opposite side may have direct rays whenever the cloud cover permits. Surely there must be an enormous difference in conditions of living and consequently of health between the one side of the valley and the other. It is widely held that a great mistake was made in the siting in the thirties of the new town of Kinlochleven in Scotland that this factor was not considered. After Dr. Garnett had studied the insolation of the deep east–west valley partly occupied by Loch Leven and the new town sited at the head of the loch, Dr. Arthur Geddes of the University of Edinburgh stigmatized this 'town of the dead end' in no uncertain terms. He pointed out that *every* aspect of climate had been ignored. A few miles down Loch Leven to the west and the inhabitants would have enjoyed more sunshine with less shadow, rain, and mist. Even on the site selected, houses were given a north exposure on northward-facing slopes, resulting in their being in deep shadow even in sunny weather. In addition they were on low ground subject to continuous down-draughts of cold air as well as being close to the fumes and smoke of the factory. Kinlochleven is far from being an isolated example. Much later houses built at Billingham had to be abandoned because they had been built without any attention being paid to prevailing winds.

Our ancestors seem in many cases to have known these facts instinctively and paid more attention to aspect in siting homes than we do today. Is it too much to say that no housing authority in even slightly hilly country should dare to lay out housing estates until insolation, as well as air drainage, has been considered? Is it also not true to say that not one authority in twenty even gives it a thought? An authority may inquire: where is the evidence that it affects health? Case studies are indeed few and this is certainly an opportunity for

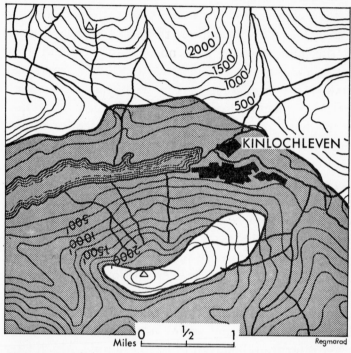

SHADED AREA IS DEPRIVED OF SUNLIGHT IN MIDWINTER, BY MOUNTAIN & HILL SHADOWS.

FIG. 25. Insolation in Loch Leven. After Alice Garnett.

the general practitioners' notebooks and files to yield comparative data of real value. Is there an advantage in living on the sunny side of the valley?

It should also be noted that air drainage and insolation—the proper term for exposure to sunshine—are very closely connected with the incidence of mist and fog. The association of fog, night and morning, with low-lying areas is well known and obvious; such sites were avoided by our ancestors for their housing. The very name *malaria* (bad air) reminds us that fever was connected in their minds with such conditions just as the French equivalent *paludisme* associates it with marshy conditions. Once again it is Professor Gilbert who has called attention to some early studies which sought to establish the connexion between such conditions and health. Dr. Henry Wentworth Acland in his *Memoir on the Cholera at Oxford in the Year 1854* (1856) published a series of detailed maps of the city which showed clearly that the worst-hit parts were the low-lying areas of the south and west. His maps gained him an international reputation and they afford us an object-lesson at the present day. They suggested a correlation with certain conditions but he did not stumble on the right answer—contaminated water. That was left, as I detailed in my first lecture, to Dr. Snow in London studying London's outbreak in the same year. Others earlier had used the mapping technique—notably Dr. Robert Baker's 'Cholera Plan' of Leeds showing that the bulk of the 700 deaths in May–November 1832 were in areas with deficient sewerage, drainage, and in need of paving, and Dr. Thomas Shapter in his *History of the Cholera in Exeter in 1832*—without getting the real answer. So it will inevitably be with our mapping today. Our maps may suggest correlations and causes, they will permit the formulation of hypotheses to be followed up, rather than any ready-made answers.

In another respect our ancestors paid great attention to microclimate. They sought shelter, especially in those parts of the country subject to south-westerly gales. My own home near the Atlantic coast of north Cornwall is a good and a typical example. For the past ten years I have been carefully restoring a small manor-house of which first records and part of the 3-foot thick stone walls date from about A.D. 1200. It nestles in a hollow facing away from the gales. Though only a few hundred yards from the cliffs it gets no sea view but the sou'-westers sweep right over—just nipping off the tops of any trees which venture to grow above 30 feet. In my walled garden and orchard I have fruit and flowers when my neighbours with a view have none.

But if our country-dwelling ancestors paid careful attention to details of site, aspect, exposure, and the like, those who moved to the towns with the industrial revolution forgot all in their haste. The slum conditions of back-to-back houses at 64 and more to the acre have often been described. We may accept that at least a goodly proportion were warm if ill-ventilated and a multitude of individual domestic chimneys belched forth their smoke to join with that from blast furnaces and factory chimneys in polluting all levels of the atmosphere and the countryside to the leeward for miles. We seem almost to have developed a pride in the soot and grime—'where there's muck there's money', Wigan became a music-hall joke, and the Black Country wore its soubriquet without shame. It is only quite recently that we have had a change of heart. The Smoke Abatement Society worked long and hard before smokeless zones were created by the Act of 1957.

There is still far to go and still much to be learnt. Physical pollution of the air is relatively easy to measure and is now expressed in milligrammes per 100 cubic metres of air. London has become comparatively clean in recent years, but in 1957–8 the average concentration

ERRATA

Page 82, line 6 from foot, for '1957' read '1956'

Page 85, Fig. 28⎫
Page 87, Fig. 29⎭ for 'J.roy.Geogr.Soc.' read 'Geogr.J.'

Stamp: Some Aspects of Medical Geography

was still over 30 in some areas. The Fuel Research
Station of D.S.I.R. (1960 Report) estimated that
London as a whole was being coated annually (1957–8)

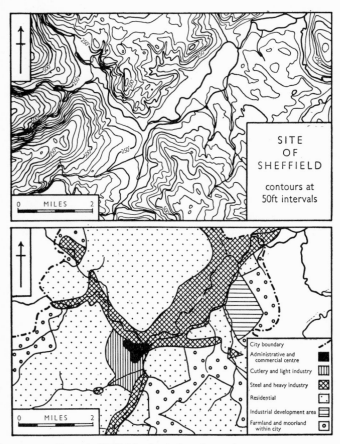

FIG. 26. Sheffield: physical setting and use zones.
[Stamp: *Applied Geography*, Penguin Books Ltd.]

with about 110,000 tons of soot and dust, in some areas
as much as 450 tons per square mile (as around Leicester
Square and in Poplar). A pioneer in this field of work
again has been Professor Alice Garnett. Her maps of

Sheffield showed almost unbelievable differences in many aspects of microclimate, including air pollution. It is scarcely surprising that Sheffield was selected for

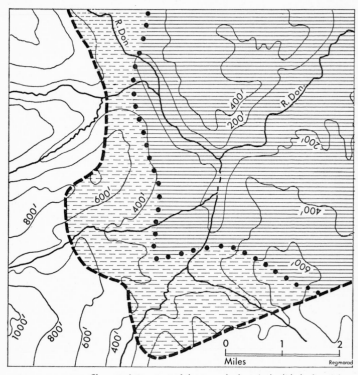

▬ ▬ ▬ ▬ ▬ Characteristic extent of the spread of smoke (solids) after 4 days
●●●●●●●●●● Characteristic extent of the spread of SO₂ (gas) after 4 days

AIR POLLUTION DURING ANTICYCLONIC CALMS IN SHEFFIELD URBAN AREA.
(BASED ON WORK CARRIED OUT IN THE DEPT. OF GEOGRAPHY, (A.GARNETT) SHEFFIELD UNIVERSITY)
FIG. 27. Sheffield: atmospheric pollution with solids and gases.

one of the first research projects in the investigation of health–climate relationships by the Medical Research Council. As so often happens, first approximations indicated the need for further work and fifty meteorological stations are to be set up within the Sheffield area.

Under the auspices of D.S.I.R. the Centre for the
Study of Air Pollution at the Warren Spring Laboratory
near Stevenage is actively engaged in continuous re-

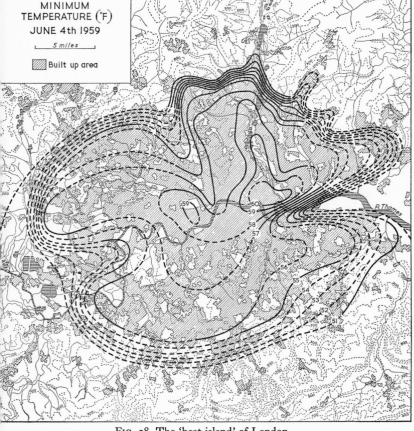

FIG. 28. The 'heat island' of London.
[Chandler, T. J. (1962), *J. roy. Geogr. Soc.*, **128**, 294.]

search. Fig. 27, to be compared with Fig. 26, gives a
sample of some results of the Sheffield work to date.

In the meantime geographers are developing and per-
fecting their methods of study of urban climates. An

interesting example of recent work is contained in the paper entitled 'London's Urban Climate' by Mr. T. J. Chandler of University College, London, who has organized since 1958 a London Climatological Survey. He deals with atmospheric pollution, fog, sunshine, wind, temperature, humidity, cloud, and precipitation, but it is in temperature studies that his novel methods have yielded some very interesting results. By using electrical resistance thermometers attached to a car, day and night traverses were made from the outskirts to the heart of London. The existence of a 'heat island' was amply demonstrated. At night minimum temperatures remain well above the surrounding green belt and the margin is surprisingly sharply defined. Similar urban heat islands have been demonstrated with other towns. Professor Gordon Manley in discussing Mr. Chandler's paper gave reasons for believing this blanket of warm air over a city would have a thickness of the order of 500 feet and that there may well be conditions when the temperature of this blanket is some 15° F. above that outside the heat island. It is fascinating to speculate further. If the range of temperature in clear summer weather is 25–30° F. and it is chill night air which is deleterious to health, it may well be that the climate in the heart of a city is far healthier than in the surrounding countryside, provided pollution can be countered or minimized.

But I am personally far from satisfied that enough is known of chemical pollution. Sulphur dioxide is important, and the Fuel Research Station estimated that 41 per cent. of pollution from this source in London came from electricity works. Combined with moisture this gas produces the highly corrosive sulphurous and sulphuric acids. I well recall an incident at Ashtead in Surrey when householders were seeking an injunction against a factory which they contended emitted corrosive sulphurous fumes. An 'expert' retained by the Company sought to refute the allegations, but he was nearly killed when a corroded wireless mast collapsed on him.

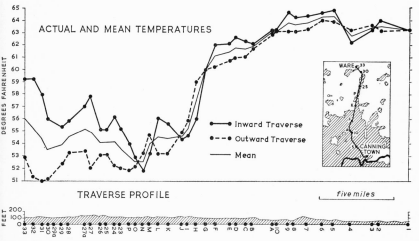

FIG. 29. A thermal traverse of London.
[Chandler, T. J. (1962), *J. roy. Geogr. Soc.*, **128**, 294.]

Many will recall the disastrous smog of December 1952, which was responsible for some 4,000 extra deaths in London and which caused the asphixiation of a number of show cattle at Olympia. I was living in a ground-floor flat in Sloane Street at the time and there was little fog but the air drifting in was noticeably foul. I had a highly polished copper warming-pan hanging in my hall which, instead of becoming tarnished, gradually took on a bright metallic sheen as if it had been chromium plated. Curiously, the parts affected were those sloping in such a way as to be influenced by particles settling through the force of gravity. The coating remained bright for months afterwards. I am waiting for a chemist to give me the full explanation of this phenomenon, but it convinced me of the vital importance of chemical pollution. The huge increase in diesel engines with their exhaust fumes near the ground, the dissipation of metal compounds now included in petrols, *must* be having an effect as yet imperfectly known or understood. Up to date there is, however, no positive evidence of this. Indeed Dr. P. J. Lawther, Director of the Air Pollution Research Unit of the Medical Research Council, asserts there is no evidence of ill-effects on those who work amid much traffic fumes.[1]

The mention of the London smog of December 1952 should serve to remind us of a simple truth but one too often forgotten. Danger lies not in the average or mean conditions but in the exceptional, and especially in the rare combination of exceptional circumstances which may occur but once in a century. The poleward limit of many species of plants (such as those described in gardeners' catalogues as 'half-hardy') is determined by the occasional long spell of cold rather than by sudden sharp frosts—as witness the elimination of the ice-plant, *Mesembryanthemum*, on some Cornish cliffs in 1947. The disastrous East Anglian sea-floods of 1953, the Lynmouth disaster of August 1952, are other examples of the rare but dangerous combination of circumstances. In the field of disease the outbreak of typhoid traced to a well contaminated by being in fissured chalk in the passage of underground water flow from a cess-pit in

[1] P. J. Lawther, *Air Pollution and its Effects on Man*, Association of Public Health Inspectors, Dawes Memorial Lecture, 1960.

the Croydon area in 1937 may be cited. Another recent example of a rare combination of adverse conditions is the disastrous cold spell of Christmas 1961 (see Howe, 1962, quoted below) when weekly deaths from bronchitis and pneumonia jumped from 1,200 at the end of November to 4,800 in the first week of January 1962 and claims for sickness benefit from 161,100 to 325,000.

The two most serious ills associated with air pollution are chronic bronchitis, a disease which in Britain kills 30,000 people a year, and causes the loss of 20 million working days, and lung cancer which claims 20,000 victims—more every year, and reaching 22,000 in 1961. With bronchitis toxic substances in the air act as irritants and so are often an indirect rather than a direct cause; smog conditions hasten rather than cause the condition and so deaths are largely with old people and children already affected. With lung cancer the position is extremely puzzling. A connection with smoking, particularly cigarette smoking, seems established, but air pollution is claimed as an important factor. But, in late Victorian times, when city airs were abundantly laden with soot, smoke and fumes, lung cancer was almost unknown. Now, as cities become cleaner, incidence is greater. Studies in both Sheffield and London suggest that smoke-free zones may actually be pockets of chemical pollution and that a high-level fog may prevent dissipation of noxious gases.

There is another aspect of air pollution of great interest and that is 'house dust'. A shaft of sunlight will often reveal the myriads of particles suspended in the atmosphere of a room. Gradually, steadily, they settle and, as every housewife knows, any dark polished surface if not dusted daily will soon show its layer of dust. It is well known that asthmatic conditions are induced in many patients by urban household dust; others are allergic to country dust, notably pollens. It seems to me there is a fascinating field here of trying to link various allergic conditions with differing types of dust. A consultant in one of our London hospitals started to map the distribution of the homes of her patients with this objective in mind: I have not yet heard of any results obtained. At present also we know very little of the character of the thousand tons of dust from space which settles daily on the earth's surface.

I am reminded of the interesting investigations of Dr. David Ordman in South Africa ('Relation of Climate to Respiratory Allergy', 1961, *Annals of Allergy*, **19,** 29–43). In this well-documented and thoughtful paper he reviews the theories and evidence to date and considers there are three possible relationships between climate and respiratory allergy:

1. Climate, especially sudden climatic change, may act as an irritant.
2. Under certain climatic conditions local house dust may be rendered more allergenic.
3. The adverse effect of climate is not due directly to such gross factors as temperature, humidity, pressure, &c., but to the state of atmospheric ionization.

In developing the second point he gives evidence that coastal house dust, developing bacteria and moulds in a damp atmosphere, is more allergenic than similar house dust even a few miles inland. But there is certainly a growing body of evidence that atmospheric ionization, qualitative and quantitative, is an important factor which may give in the future a scientific explanation why sufferers from 'rheumatism' have so long claimed to be influenced by weather, why asthmatic patients are affected by the passage of fronts, why arthritic attacks are associated in Iceland with the aurora borealis. The beneficial qualities of mountain air may be associated with negative ionization, whereas positive ionization is harmful. Far too little is yet known of the state of ionization under air-conditioning, and whether there is a harmful increase of positive ions. We may even find atomic fall-out to have, in certain circumstances, a beneficial influence.

There is a considerable body of evidence that it is the *suddenness* of climatic change which constitutes a major danger. Since we subject ourselves, through the tropical climates we are now creating indoors, to such sudden changes there may well be a linkage with increase of chronic bronchitis which is bothering us in our towns. A Sheffield iron-master with whom I served in the First World War has recently put before me an interesting suggestion. In iron and steel works men are working under conditions of very high temperature, with much pollution of the air by smoke and fumes, sweating freely. Formerly at the end of the day's work a man would wind his sweatband round his neck, put on his coat, trudge home to his back-to-back to the warmth of a heaped coal fire and little ventilation. Today he works under similar conditions but at the end of the day stands in a chill wind in the bus queue, gets out in the keen evening air at 500 feet, walks thoroughly chilled to his semi-detached home in an open-density housing estate, where an electric fire in the sitting-room is no substitute for the old, warm, fuggy kitchen. He is being killed by the increase in living standard he has achieved.

Modern town planners almost worship 'open density' as if space were an objective in itself. Many of our older towns could, a few still can, be described as 'cosy'. That is an adjective which can rarely be applied to a new town. It seems to me that we are doing much today which is highly inconsistent. We seem to have decided that for our offices, hotels, and to a less extent our factories, man should be treated as a tropical or near-tropical animal. Similarly with illness the command has long been and still is, keep the patient warm and don't forget the hot-water bottle. But, perhaps with a waning influence, the fresh-air fiend is still with us with his insane worship of open windows and consequent draughts. Have we not something, perhaps much, to learn from hibernating animals? Their long period of rest is made possible, I believe, by the minimum of fresh air with which their bodies are required to deal. Where only a small quantity of cold air reaches the lungs, heat loss is small. *Verb. sap.!*

In view of the fact that we are continuing to build new towns, is it not possible to secure an objective review of health conditions in some already well established—one thinks of Welwyn Garden City, Letchworth, Crawley, Stevenage, Peterlee, and others—for comparison with older established towns of comparable size?

I deliberately bring in this uncertain and controversial note, because I want to emphasize how little we know and how much there is to be investigated. Very recently Dr. Melvyn Howe has adopted Siple's concept of 'windchill'—the cooling power of wind and temperature combinations on the human skin, dry and shaded—

from the Antarctic to Britain. Provisional results emphasize the advantages of south-east England, and suggest that contrary to popular belief periods of dry cold are particularly dangerous in Britain.

It is satisfactory to be able to record the increasing attention now being given to various aspects of medical geography. I would first mention the continuing work of the Medical Research Unit under Dr. May at the American Geographical Society in New York. It is my hope that the joint Medical Geography Committee of the Royal Geographical Society and the B.M.A. will not be content with the atlas of diseases it has just completed under Dr. Howe but will continue to inspire and support further work. Then there is the Commission on Medical Geography (Ecology of Health and Disease) of the International Geographical Union. In the intervals between its periodic Congresses—normally every four years—the Union works by means of Commissions, some charged with a specific and limited task, others of the nature of standing commissions to carry on work over longer periods and to act in an advisory capacity to the 50-odd member countries. The Medical Geography Commission was set up at the Lisbon Congress in 1949, and its *First Report* to the Washington Congress of 1952 (unfortunately out of print) included a general review of the History, Definitions, and Problems of Medical Geography by Dr. May, the Chairman, together with important contributions by D. H. K. Lee (Johns Hopkins), Arthur Geddes (Edinburgh), and Max Sorre (Paris). The *Second Report* presented to the Rio Congress of 1956—also unfortunately out of print—and the Third presented at Stockholm in 1960 (published in brief in *International Geographical Union Newsletter*, vol. XI,

1960, 8–13) record work in progress in several parts of the world.

It is encouraging to know that the pioneer work of Professor Alice Garnett on the microclimatology (including air pollution) of Sheffield is being continued and is being linked with the Medical Research Council's Group for Research on Atmospheric Pollution directed by Dr. P. J. Lawther of St. Bartholomew's Hospital. Reference has already been made to the active Air Pollution Division of the Warren Spring Laboratory of the Department of Scientific and Industrial Research which held a two-day symposium on 7–8 November 1962. There is also the work under Mr. Chandler at University College, London. Other universities have taken and are taking an active interest in similar studies of urban climates—Edinburgh (A. Macpherson), Leicester (Norman Pye), and studies have been made at Bath (W. G. V. Balchin and N. Pye), Manchester, Nottingham, and Reading.

At the international level, a vast field of work comes within the sphere of WHO (World Health Organization) and it is to be hoped that mapping techniques will play an increasing part in the investigations sponsored or encouraged by that body.

The scourge of cancer is so terrible that surely no stone should be left unturned in the effort to bring it under control. According to figures given in 1962 by WHO, over 2 million people are definitely known to die of one or another of the many forms of cancer every year; cancer sufferers definitely number over 5 million and more than 20 million are known to be affected by some form of precancerous condition with the likelihood of the development of a malignant tumour. What little is known of the geographical distribution of different forms of cancer seems to offer nothing but the most baffling paradoxes. The Russians, through the Academy of Medical Sciences of the U.S.S.R., have pioneered in the investigation of the geographical distribution of the disease. Specially equipped expeditions under the leadership of Dr. A. V. Chaklin, now head of the cancer unit of WHO, obtained definite evidence that incidence of skin cancers increased with exposure to ultra-violet radiation of the sun, i.e. sun-bathing, at least among white-skinned peoples. Skin cancer is four times as prevalent on the shores of the Black Sea as it is on the shores of the Baltic, accounting for a quarter of all malignant tumours. It may well be that voluntary exposure to the sun's rays may be more dangerous than the much-publicized 'fall-out' from atomic explosions.

Cancer brings us back to air pollution again. Some years ago the prevalence of cancer among chimney sweeps led to the conclusion that certain tar-compounds in soot might have definite carcinogenic properties.

It is well known that some of the greatest discoveries of science have been made almost by accident. They are certainly the result of careful observations of unanticipated phenomena. Pasteur was seeking the origin of life when he stumbled upon the whole bacterial world; penicillin was likewise a chance discovery. The geographer in his constant urge to make maps may likewise stumble upon the unexpected. The story is nearly always the same: a map reveals a pattern and poses the question, Why? Attempts to answer that insistent question often lead to hypotheses which further work shows to be untenable. For example, parts of lowland England can be shown to be characterized by scattered, isolated dwellings, other parts by nucleated settlements. In India such differences are associated with the prevalence or otherwise of the social custom of purdah. In lowland Britain scattered dwellings are characteristic of grassland and animal husbandry, nucleated settlements with arable land and crop farming. One could develop theories of Abel being near his flocks and herds, Cain sharing his farm implements with his kinsmen. But the grassland is associated with clay soils, the arable with well-drained loams; and the real answer is water— plenty of surface water, hence ponds and streams on the clays, but water available only from certain points, notably springs, on the loams: hence a village near an assured supply.

When population distribution is mapped carefully in the tropics, there are usually marked patterns. In parts of West Africa the settlements were found always to avoid river banks despite the fact that the cattle had to be taken daily to the river for drinking, the women had a long arduous journey to draw their supplies from the river. Danger of flood? No, that was not the answer because plenty of flood-free sites were available. The people concerned simply said it was what their ancestors had always done. The true answer was found eventually to be determined by the distribution of 'river blindness' caused by parasites carried by a fly, *Simulium*, breeding in a riverside situation. The headwaters of the White Volta in northern Ghana are almost uninhabited because of the prevalence of this fly.

I bring this brief survey of a vast field to an end by appealing once again for a collaboration of workers in the several fields which meet in the study of the ecology of man and above all with the request: Put it on a map.

APPENDIX

Notes on Sources of Material

THE basic statistical material on world mortality is contained in the *Demographic Yearbook* published annually by the Statistical Office of the United Nations Organization in New York (especially 1957 and 1961), together with other special publications. Statistical material for the United Kingdom is contained in *The Registrar General's Statistical Review* (for England and Wales, Scotland, and Northern Ireland); also *Decennial Supplements*.

Dr. Jacques M. May has collected and digested a vast amount of material in his three volumes in the *Studies in Medical Geography*, sponsored by the American Geographical Society of New York, Vol. 1, *The Ecology of Human Disease* (1958), Vol. 2, *Studies in Disease Ecology* (1961), Vol. 3, *The Ecology of Malnutrition in the Far and Near East* (1961). These are indispensable: they must be used with the seventeen published sheets of the *Atlas of Diseases*, also issued by the Society (1950–5).

During the war the Germans issued an *Atlas of Epidemic Diseases* (Seuchen Atlas) under the editorship of H. Zeiss, which covered areas then of military importance to Germany (Gotha, 1941–5). This was enlarged to form the *World Atlas of Epidemic Diseases* (Welt–Seuchen Atlas) under the editorship of E. Rodenwaldt (Hamburg, 1952, 1956).

The World Health Organization, Geneva, publishes the *Manual of the International Statistical Classification of Diseases, Injuries, and Causes of Death* (two volumes, 1957).

The *National Atlas of Disease Mortality* published under the auspices of the Royal Geographical Society and edited by G. Melvyn Howe, 1963, is indispensable for the United Kingdom: it has a long introduction including an historical review with full references to previous work, including A. Haviland's classic, *Geographical Distribution of Disease in Great Britain* (London, 1875).

Most of the papers and detailed works quoted in the preceding chapters have extensive bibliographies, and since it is essentially the nature of medical geography to lie on the borderland of several disciplines, relevant material is likely to be found in a very wide range of scientific works and periodicals.

Amongst general works of broad relevant interest may be noted:

K. M. BUCHANAN and J. C. PUGH, *Land and People in Nigeria*, pp. 41–57, London, University of London Press, 1955.

G. H. T. KIMBLE, *Tropical Africa*, vol. ii, pp. 33–51, 159–82, New York, Twentieth-Century Fund, 1960.

D. H. K. LEE, *Climate and Economic Development in the Tropics*, New York, Harper, 1957.

S. F. MARKHAM, *Climate and the Energy of Nations*, London, Oxford University Press, 1942.

CLARENCE MILLS, *Climate Makes the Man*, London, Gollancz, 1944.

PAUL B. SEARS, *The Ecology of Man*, Condon Lectures, Eugene, Oregon. Oregon State System of Higher Education.

L. DUDLEY STAMP, *Africa: A Study in Tropical Development*, New York, Wiley, 1953; second edition, 1964.

—— (editor), *The History of Land Use in Arid Regions* (also in French), Paris, UNESCO, 1961.

—— *Our Developing World*, London, Faber, 1960; reprinted 1961.

All the papers quoted above in the text may be regarded as important contributions to the development of ideas or as outstanding specialist studies. Especially valuable are the following:

R. W. ARMSTRONG, 'Cancer and Soil: Review and Counsel', *The Professional Geographer*, 14, 1962, 7–13.

T. J. CHANDLER, 'London's Urban Climate,' *Geog. Jour.*, 128, 1962, 279–302.

E. W. Gilbert, 'Pioneer Maps of Health and Disease in England', *Geog. Jour.*, **124**, part 2, 1958, 172–83.

G. Melvyn Howe, 'The Geographical Distribution of Cancer Mortality in Wales, 1947–53', *Trans. and Papers Inst. Brit. Geographers*, **28**, 1960, 189–213. See also *Brit. J. prev. soc. Med.*, **13**, 1959, 204–10.

—— 'The Geographical Variation of Disease Mortality in England and Wales in the Mid-Twentieth Century', *Advancement of Science*, Jan. 1961, 415–25.

—— 'Windchill, Absolute Humidity and the Cold Spell of Christmas 1961', *Weather*, **17**, 1962, 349–58.

A. T. A. Learmonth, 'Some Contrasts in the Regional Geography of Malaria in India and Pakistan', *Trans. and Papers Inst. Brit. Geographers*, **23**, 1957, 37–59.

—— 'Medical Geography in Indo-Pakistan', *India Geog. Jour.*, **33**, 1958.

——'Medical Geography in India and Pakistan', *Geog. Jour.*, **127**, 1961, 10–26.

INDEX

INDEX

Acland, H. W., *Memoir of Cholera*, 81.
Aëdes aegypti, 21.
Africa, arid and wet regions, 17.
Air pollution, chemical, 86, 87.
— — measurement, 57, 82, 83, 87.
Air-conditioning, 41, 46–53.
Allen, Sir George, 73.
Allergens, 90.
American Geographical Society, maps on distribution of disease, 3.
Ankylostomiasis, 22.
Anopheles, 11, 21, 70, 73.
Armstrong, R. W., on cancer and soil, 98.
Atlas of Diseases, 2, 6, 97.
Atlas of Epidemic Diseases, 97.
Atmospheric pollution, 57, 82, 83, 86, 87.

Baker, R., 81.
Balchin, Professor W. G. V., 94.
Bejel, world distribution, 6.
Bengal, population changes, 69, 70.
Bentley, C. A., 70.
Bibliography, 97.
Bilharziasis, 23.
Bonacina, L. C. W., 36.
'Break-bone' fever, 22.
Bronchitis, 89.
— deaths, distribution in England and Wales, 62, 63, 64, 65.
Buchanan, K. M., and Pugh, J. C., *Land and People in Nigeria*, 7, 98.
Buildings, air-conditioning, 41, 46–53.
— central heating, 42–44.
Bush, R., 77.

Cancer and soil, 98.
— geographical distribution, 94, 95.
— mortality, geographical distribution in Wales, 98.
— relation to climate, 31.
Central heating, 42, 43, 44.
Chaklin, A. V., 95.
Chandler, T. J., on London's urban climate, 85, 86, 94, 98.
Cholera, 81.
— Broad Street outbreak, 15.

Cholera, distribution, 6, 12, 13, 14, 15.
Chrenko, F. A., on human factors in heating, 45.
Christophers, S. R., 70, 71.
Climate and disease, 1–25.
— and economic development in the tropics, 32.
— and health, 26–53, 77, 78, 83.
— effect on behaviour, 33, 36.
— relation to energy, 29, 30.
Clothing in the tropics, 39.
Cold, effect on growth and development, 30.

Death rates, 57–63.
Demographic Yearbook, 28, 97.
Dengue, 6, 22.
Disease as environmental factor in national or regional development, 7.
— cartography, 1–4, 6.
— classification, W. H. O. *Manual*, 97.
— geographical analysis, 1, 97.
Dust, household, 89.
Dwellings, healthy aspect for, 77.

Elephantiasis, 22.
Energy in relation to climate, 29, 30, 98.

Freyche, M.-J., 23.
Furneaux, B., 77.

Garnett, Professor A., 79, 83, 94.
Geddes, A., 73, 79, 93.
Geographical analysis of disease, 1.
Geography, medical, 93.
Gilbert, E. W., on pioneer maps of health and disease in England, 81, 98.
Glossina morsitans, 18.
— *palpalis*, 18.

Haviland, A., *Geographical Distribution of Disease in Great Britain*, 77, 97.
Heart disease, distribution, 65.

PRINTED IN GREAT BRITAIN
AT THE UNIVERSITY PRESS, OXFORD
BY VIVIAN RIDLER
PRINTER TO THE UNIVERSITY